THE SCRIBNER
RADIO MUSIC LIBRARY

Edited by
ALBERT E. WIER

VOLUME VII

SONGS FROM THE OPERAS

SACRED MUSIC

. . .

VOCAL
PIANO

NEW YORK

CHARLES SCRIBNER'S SONS

THE SCRIBNER RADIO MUSIC LIBRARY

VOLUME VII—OPERATIC SONGS AND SACRED MUSIC

TABLE OF CONTENTS—TITLES

A Guide Through Volume VII

THE volumes of the SCRIBNER RADIO MUSIC LIBRARY are devoted entirely to compositions which are heard constantly over the great broadcasting chains—played by orchestras, chamber music organizations, or instrumental soloists; sung by choral organizations or by vocal soloists. Each of the nine volumes contains only the choicest and most popular of its particular type of music.

This volume opens with a series of grand opera songs so well established in the graces of the radio audience that one or more of them is sure to be heard whenever a programme of operatic music is broadcast.

GRAND OPERA SONGS
It is quite a matter of surprise to note how many tenor arias from the grand operas are radio favorites. From "Il Trovatore" we may at once select Manrico's **Ah! I Have Sighed to Rest Me**; from "Martha" Lionel's **Ah! So Pure,** in praise of Lady Harriet; from Donizetti's "Elixir of Love" Nemorino's languishing **A Furtive Tear**; from "La Gioconda" Enzo's dramatic **Heaven and Ocean**; from "Aïda" Rhadames's rapturous **Heav'nly Aïda**; from "Manon" the despairing **I Am Alone,** sung by Des Grieux; from "Le Cid" Rodrigo's moving **Prayer**; from "Rigoletto" the Duke of Mantua's cynical **Woman Is Fickle**; from "I Pagliacci" Canino's heartbroken **Vesti la Giubba**; from "Cavalleria Rusticana" Turridu's extravagantly amorous **Siciliana**; and from Tschaikowsky's gloomy "Eugene Onégin" Lenski's passionate air, **Yes, I Love You.**

For baritones, songs such as the **Evening Star** from "Tannhäuser" and the **Toreador Song** from "Carmen" are radio favorites; for contraltos arias such as the **Habañera** from "Carmen" and **My Heart at Thy Sweet Voice** from Saint-Saëns's "Samson and Delilah." There are many soprano arias familiar to and beloved of the radio audience—the exquisite **Know'st Thou Yonder Land?** from "Mignon," the pathetic **Lovely Flowers, I Pray** from "Faust," the folk-song, **Last Rose of Summer,** from "Martha," the serene **Lullaby** from Godard's "Jocelyn," and the colorful **Song of India** from Rimsky-Korsakow's "Sadko." In duet form we often hear the **Evening Prayer** from "Hansel and Gretel," the mournful **Home to Our Mountains** from "Il Trovatore," and the languorous barcarolle, **Lovely Night,** from the "Tales of Hoffman."

SACRED MUSIC
For those who are fond of religious music, either vocal or instrumental, there is a veritable feast in sacred selections broadcast, particularly on Sunday, and many of these compositions are to be found in this volume, comprising selections for the piano, sacred songs, negro spirituals, and familiar hymns.

PIANO SELECTIONS
In the piano transcription section will be found the **Andante Religioso,** by François Thomé; the celebrated **Andantino,** by the distinguished organist, Edwin H. Lemare; the **Angel's Serenade,** by the Italian 'cellist, Gaetano Braga; a descriptive meditation by Jules Massenet titled **The Angelus**; and transcriptions of both the **Ave Maria** of Franz Schubert and the **Ave Maria** of Charles Gounod, the latter founded on the Bach Prelude in C Major. Other compositions included in this section are the **Bridal March** from Wagner's "Lohengrin," the

Funeral March from the Sonata, Op. 25, by Frederic Chopin, the **Hallelujah Chorus** from Handel's "Messiah," the **Inflammatus** from Rossini's "Stabat Mater," the **Largo** by Handel, and an arrangement for piano of the ancient Jewish sacred melody, the **Kol Nidrei.**

SACRED SONGS

Another important section in this volume is that devoted to some of the sacred songs which are familiar to the radio audience. Foremost among these may be mentioned the Bach-Gounod **Ave Maria,** and another exquisite **Ave Maria** by Franz Schubert, the latter set to words taken from Sir Walter Scott's famous poem, the "Lady of the Lake." Then there is Gounod's beautiful song, **There Is a Green Hill Far Away,** and the lovely **No Shadows Yonder** from Gaul's cantata, "The Holy City"; the contralto aria, so peaceful in its musical content, **O Rest in the Lord,** from Mendelssohn's "Elijah"; and the appealing, simple **Prayer** sung by Agatha in Weber's "Der Freischutz." This section also contains nine sacred songs in what may be termed the popular vein—**Calvary,** by Rodney; **A Dream of Paradise,** by Gray; **Hosanna,** by Jules Granier (so well sung by Enrico Caruso); **Jerusalem,** by Henry Parker; **The Lost Chord,** by Sir Arthur Sullivan; **One Sweetly Solemn Thought,** by Ambrose; **Over the Stars There Is Rest,** by Franz Abt; **The Palms,** written by the celebrated French baritone, Jean Baptiste Faure; and a favorite sacred song for bass voices, **Rocked in the Cradle of the Deep.**

NEGRO SPIRITUALS

The popularity of negro spirituals with the radio audience is unquestioned—it never seems to tire of hearing them, whether at the Philharmonic Stadium concerts with the Hall Johnson Choir or as sung by some individual of lesser note. The number of songs reputed to be genuine spirituals is considerably over four hundred—many of these, however, are regarded as spurious—and the twenty to be found in this volume are representative not only of the best from a musical point of view, but also from the standpoint of popularity with the radio listener. These spirituals were originally musical outpourings of religious faith at camp-meetings held in the South, and each one embodies a distinct religious thought. For example, the desire for salvation is the theme of spirituals such as **"Steal Away," "Deep River," "Roll, Jordan, Roll," "All God's Chillun Got Wings," "Keep a-Inchin' Along,"** and **"Peter, Go Ring Dem Bells."** Christ's immolation on the Cross is the subject of **"Were You There?"** and **"Crucifixion"**; the efficacy of prayer is enlarged upon in **"Ev'ry Time I Feel the Spirit," "I Couldn't Hear Nobody Pray,"** and **"I'm a-Rolling"**; resignation is the theme of **"Nobody Knows De Trouble I've Seen"** and **"Sometimes I Feel Like a Motherless Child."** It is, of course, the touching simplicity of the melodies and the unwavering faith of the words which stamp spirituals as genuine expressions of religious devotion, and that is unquestionably the reason for their great popularity.

HYMNS

This volume appropriately closes with a section devoted to about seventy hymns that are everlasting favorites with that part of the radio audience who incline to religious services and programmes. The list includes all those hymns which have become corner-stones in the musical structure of religious faith, such as **Abide With Me, Lead, Kindly Light, Nearer, My God, to Thee** and **Rock of Ages.**

A Song of India

(Sadko)

N. Rimsky - Korsakow

Sweet__ its song is fall - - - -ing;

Heav'n a - bove re - call - - - -ing;__

Brill- - - - -iant plum - - - -age glan - - - -cing__

Fade____ the scene____ en tran - - - -cing,-

All_____ who hear_____ this sing - - - er_____ Would_____ for-

-ev - - - er lin - - ger. Thy lof-ty hills are rich be-yond all

dream-ing, Be-neath thy wa-ters love-ly pearls be gleam-ing, O beau-teous

land! Oh, In - di - a!_____

Heav'nly Aïda
(Aïda)

G. Verdi

Moderato

Andantino expressivo

Heav'n - ly — A - ï - da beau - ty — re-splen - dent Ra - di - ant

cresc. *p*

flow - er bloom - ing— and bright; Queen - ly—thou reign - est

cresc.

o'er me tran - scend - ent, Bath-ing my spir-it in beau - ty's light.

espressivo

cresc.

Would thou thy bright skies once more be - hold - ing, Breath-ing the

soft airs of thy na - tive land, Round thy fair brow a di - a - dem

fold - ing, Thine were a throne _____ next the sun to stand. Ah! _____

Heav'n - -ly _ A - ï - -da, Beau - -ty _ re-splend - ent,

cresc.

Ra - - di - - ant flow - - ers, bloom - - ing - - and

bright; Queen - - ly - thou reign - est o'er me tran -

scend - ent, Bath - ing my spi - rit in beau - ty's light, my spi - rit in beauty's

light, my spi - rit in beau - ty's light. _____

Habanera
(Carmen)

G. Bizet

he who doth cold - ly slight thee, Thou for thy mas - ter__ oft thou'lt
seize him, ah! he gets free__ He'd be the mas - ter,__ thee the

choose.__ Ah, love!__ Ah, love!__
slave.__

Ah, love!__ Ah, love! For love he

is the lord of all, and ne'er law's i - cy fet-ters will he wear, If thou me

Toreador Song

(Carmen)

G. Bizet

floor to___ roof!___ For wild with joy___ the peo-ple speak of you___ Each one of
his re - treat!___ Al - read - y pierc - ed thro' a horse has fall - en, Dragging

them of you_____ is___ speak - ing___ Clam-or - ing all___
down a stal - - wart pic - a - dor!___ Bra - vo! the mob shrieks.

Wild quest - ions ask - ing All are shout-ing till___ the com - bat is o'er,___
Bra - vo! the mob shrieks He___ goes, he comes, he rush - es____ on!___

See the crowds, of you they're speak - ing___ Of you they're speak - ing___ and questions

He tries___ to tear the ban-drol down,___ He goes, he comes, with___ a sav-age

ask - ing___

roar!___

'Tis a fes - ti-val rare of its kind,___

Now with blood___ the reek-ing ring is full___

Come now then,___ be on your guard

Ter - ror throbs___ in ev'- ry heart

At-tend! at - tend! at-tend! at-

tend!___ Ah!___

Tor- e - a-dor e'er watch-ful___ be___

Tor - e - a - dor,___ Tor - e - a - dor,___ Do not forget the bright - est of eyes___

Fond-ly thee a - wait!___ and love is the prize, yes__love's the prize!___

Waits thee Oh, Tor - ea - dor!___ dor! Yes__love's the___

prize that__waits Tor - ea - dor!__ That waits Tor - ea - dor!___

I Dreamt that I Dwelt in Marble Halls

(Bohemian Girl)

M. W. Balfe

Siciliana
(Cavalleria Rusticana)

P. Mascagni

O Lo-la,___ with thy cheeks ros-ier than cher--ries!___ Crown'd is thy soul with love ev-er more glow---ing!___ Fain would I kiss thy lips, ah! so be-guil-ing!___

Favored by heav-en would I be, such bliss know- - - -ing.

But tho' thy thresh-old crim-son blood is stain - ing

E-ven 'twere mine thy love would be still the gain- -ing

And tho' I lost my life thy love to be gain - ing, Thy love to me__ would

still be all— sus-tain - - -ing! And tho' I lost my

life thy love to be gain - ing, Thy love to me— would still be all— sus-

dim.

dolce *dim. poco a poco*

tain - - -ing! Ah!_____ Ah!_____

perdendosi

Ah!_____ Ah!_____

A Furtive Tear
(Elixir of Love)

G. Donizetti

Down her fair cheek a fur-tive tear____ stole from her eyes____ so dark; Tell-ing their gay and hap-py cheer, it pained her heart to mark; Where-fore her pres-ence fly? Where-fore her dear pres-ence

fly? Where all her love she's re -

veal - ing, re-veal - - -ing?

Might I but feel her beat-ing heart, rest - ing a - gainst my

own; Could I my feel - ing sweet impart, and

min - gle sigh with sigh. But feel her heart's beat close a-gainst my

own, But feel her heart's beat close against my own

Free-ly I then would die, all her love know-ing, all know - -ing Ah!

glad-ly I then, I then would die, Ah! glad-ly I then would die, I would die.

Prayer
(Le Cid)

J. Massenet

O Sov - er - eign,__ O Judge, O Fa - ther! Al - ways on high__ With me__ al - way;__ I wor-ship thee in times of joy and still I bless thee in the vale of tears, I go far a - way from__ this cold world, Free__ from all hu - man re -

grets; O Sov - er - eign;___ O Judge,___ O Fa - ther

Ev - er in my heart your im - age rest - eth, And in thy hands, put I my

fate!___ O Sov - er - eign!___ O Judge!___ O

Fa - - - - - - ther!

Yes, I Love You
(Eugene Onègin)

P. Tschaikowsky

L'istesso tempo

molto espressivo

Yes, I love you, you a - lone, my Ol - ga, you I

love_ with a fire___ Whose burn - ing ar - dor pas - sion_ gla - moured, May but the

po - - et's soul, the po-et's soul in - spire! One constant

bright-est smile,— your kind-est glanc - es, As we in woodland shade were

stay - ing, True com-rades hap-pi - ly were play-ing. Ah!— yes, I

love you, dear, yes, I love you, dear, with a po - et's ar - -dor

deep and o - ver-whelm-ing; My each dream your charm makes clear - er, My each

yearn - ing holds you dear - er, Joy or grief each brings you near - er; For I love you dear, yes I love you with an ar-dent fire, Which soars o'er pain and joy in its de-sire, Which part-ing's grief may nev-er slay, Nor meet-ing's joy al - lay, Whose pas-sion not e - ter - ni - ty it - self⸺ may tire!

Lovely Flowers I Pray
(Faust)

C. Gounod

Love - ly flow - ers I pray,_____ my
Speak, oh flow - ers, for me,_____ I

love_____ be - tray,_____
trust_____ in thee,_____

Tell her she's my sole treas - - ure,
Teach her, ah, to dis - cov - er

Tell her, ah, once a - gain_____ my heart's____ sore pain,____
And my own bos - om's fire_____ her heart____ in - spire,____

My____ heart's, my heart's____ sore pain,
Her____ heart, my her heart____ in - spire,

My____ heart's, my heart's____ sore pain!____
Her____ heart, her heart____ in - spire!____

Heaven! and Ocean!

(La Gioconda)

A. Ponchielli

Heav — en! And o - cean! Yon e - the-real veil is

ra - di - ant as ho - ly al — — tar. My

an - gel, will she come from heav — en? My an - gel, will she come o'er o - cean?

Here in dark — ness I am wait — — — ing, wild - ly

Vesti la Giubba

(I Pagliacci)

R Leoncavallo

I Am Alone

(Manon)

J. Massenet

I'm a - lone!

A-lone at last, the fate-ful mo - ment now has come.

From sor-did care I'm free____ and

I but seek the hav- en of rest life can give. Yes, I shall

put my faith in God be-twixt the world and me!

Ah! de-part, vis- ion fair! Leave me now in peace

List- en, pray, to my plea, Calm my sad, lone- ly heart.

To its depths I have quaffed Life's sad_ cup of woe!_____

Yet have I not complained Tho' it seem'd filled so full_____

Ah! de-part, de-part, vis-ion fair!_ Ah, de-part_____ far from

me_____ far_from me!_____

Evening Prayer

(Hansel and Gretel)

E. Humperdinck

Moderato quasi Andante

When I lay me down in bed,

An - gel guards are 'round me spread: Two at my head pray - ing,

Two at my feet stay - ing, Two up - on my right hand,

Two up-on my left stand, Two to dream-land take me,

Two at dawn-ing wake me, Two there are who tar-ry, To

Heav'n my soul to car - - -ry!

Sextette from "Lucia"

(Lucia di Lammermoor)

Solo Arrangement

G. Donizetti

guilt____ thy_ heart are_ rend_ -ing, Thy de - spair_ -ing looks dis -
earth____ have both be - tray'd____ me Love, do thou____ with cour - age

1.

arm___ me, Faith-less maid - en, faith - less maid, a - las I love! 'Twas my

2.

arm_____ me,_ give_ me strength, oh give____ me strength to do thy

will. Day_ of wrath_____ what will be_ thy end_ -ing, Oh_ day_ of

wrath____ what will be___ thy end — — ing,____ May heav — en with__ cour - age

arm me, May heav — — en give_____ me

strength____ to do__ thy will. Ah! like a rose____ 'mid__ tem - pest

bend — ing,____ Fur - ther grief____ may__ be__ im - pend — ing,____ Oh

love _____ with _ cour - age arm me, with _ cour - _ - age

calando

arm _____ me to do _ thy will, _____ to _ do _ thy will, Oh give me

strength to do _____ thy _____ will, Oh give me strength to do thy will.

Un-grateful maid I love, _____ love thee still! _____

In Happy Moments Day by Day

(Maritana)

W. V. Wallace

hap - - py mo-ments day by day, The sands of life___ may
an - -xious eyes up-on us gaze And hearts with fond - ness

pass, In swift but tran-quil tide a - way, From
beat, Whose smile up-on each fea-ture plays With

time's un - err - - ing glass.
truth - ful - ness re - plete.

Yet hopes we used as
Some thoughts none oth - - er

bright to deem, Re - mem - brance will___ re - call; Whose
can re - place Re - mem - brance will___ re - call; Which

pure and whose un-fad-ing beam, Is dear - er than___them all, Whose
in the flight of years we trace Is dear - er than___them all, Which

pure and whose un-fad-ing beam, Is___ dear - er than them all.
in the flight of years we trace Is___ dear - er than them all.

Ah! So Pure
(Martha)

F. Flotow

Like a beam from a - bove Heav'n ly

ra - di-ant she ap - peared; Bliss - ful dream,

star of love to my heart re-mains en - deared_____ Pierced this

Like a beam from a-bove Heav'n - ly ra - di - ant

she ap - peared Bliss - ful dream star of love ___

cresc.

___ to my heart re - mains en - deared Mar - tha, Mar - tha

dim. _f_

thou'rt de - parted ___ and hast sunk this heart in love

Thou didst leave me bro - ken heart - ed soon to

my lone grave I'll go Ah!

to my grave I'll go, Ah! I'll go.

The Last Rose of Summer
(Martha)

F. Flotow

'Tis the last rose_ of_ sum - mer, Left_
I'll not leave thee,_ thou_ lone one, To_

bloom - ing a - -lone; All her love - ly_ com -
pine_ on the stem; Since the love - ly_ are_

pan - ions, are_ fad - -ed and_ gone; No_
sleep - ing, go_ sleep_ thou with them._ Thus_

flow — — ers of her kin — dred, No___ rose — — bud is
kind — — — ly I scat — ter Thy___ leaves___ o'er the

nigh,___ To re - flect back___ her___ blush - es, Or___
bed,___ Where thy mates of___ the___ gar - den, Lie

give___ sigh for sigh.
scent - less and___ dead. Where thy mates of___ the___

gar - den, Lie___ scent - less___ and dead.

Know'st Thou Yonder Land?

(Mignon)

A. Thomas

Know - est thou yon - der land,
Know - est thou yon - der land,

where the or - -ange grows?___ Where___ the fruit is of
with its walls___ of pride?___ Vast___ and state - ly

gold,_____ and so fair___ the rose?___ Where the breeze
halls,_____ where all splen-dour a - bide?___ Where___ mar - ble

gent - ly wafts___ the___ songs___ of birds;_____
stat - ues grand___ all a - round you may see;_____

here? 'Tis with thee I would fly, 'Tis there!__ 'Tis there my heart's love o-

bey- -ing 'Twere bliss to live and to die,_____ 'Tis

there my heart's love o- bey- -ing I'd live, I_____ would

die.

Evening Star
(Tannhäuser)

R. Wagner

Thou star re - splen - - dent, pure_____ and bright,

'Mid hu - man life's_____ dull shade_____ and gloom,

Pour now o'er us thy stream_____ of light,

Shine clear from heav- -en, as - suage____ our doom.

Ere long a soul to thee____ a - scend - -ing

Grace re- -flect____ thy light____ ex - tend - -ing,

pp un poco ritard.

Ere long a soul to thee____ a -

scend - -ing, .Will grace re - -flect thy_____

light_____ ex - tend - -ing!

Woman Is Fickle

(Rigoletto)

G. Verdi.

Wom - an is fick - le, false al - to - geth - er;
Wretch-ed the day is when she looks kind - ly;

Moves like a feath - er,
Trusts to her blind - ly,

borne on the breez - es Wom - an with witch-ing smile, will e'er de - ceive you,
He life thus wast - ing Yet he must sure - ly be dull be-yond meas - ure,

My Heart At Thy Sweet Voice

(Samson and Delilah)

C. Saint-Saëns

Lovely Night
(Tales of Hoffman)

J. Offenbach

Love - ly night whose star - ry smile Our ten - der rap - ture bless — es, Night of love, our love— the while With thy— ca - ress be - guile! Short is life, the hours they fly, And

ar - dent lips meet, Let our ar - dent lips meet! Ah!

Love - ly night, whose star - ry smile, Our ten - der rap - ture

bless - es, Night of love, our love the while, With thy ca - ress be -

guile. O night whose star - ry smile Ah! Our love's sweet rap - ture

Lullaby

(Jocelyn)

B. Godard

Con – cealed from ev'– ry eye, Where Prov – i –dence has led,

How sad the mo-ments fly, How long the nights and dread! And yet re-pose is sweet, We have slept un-re-pin-ing, And we've prayed while the wake-ful stars a-bove were shin--ing.

Andante

Oh, may thy dream not soon be o'er,_____ For an-gels hov-er near thy

Ah! I Have Sighed to Rest Me.

(Il Trovatore)

G. Verdi

Andante Sostenuto

(CHORUS OF NUNS)

Have com-pas-sion up-on a soul de-part-ing, For that a-

bode from whence there's no re-turn-ing; Thy for-giv-ness, ah! pow'r di-vine im-

part-ing Let him not be a prey to end-less burn-ing.

(LEONORA)

That sol-emn pe-

ti- -tion, so sad-ly a-scend-ing, With ter-ror and

mys - ter - y   the air seems to   fill!   'Gainst' fa - tal fore -

bod - ing,   my heart is con - tend - ing; My breath is sus - pend - ed, my puls - es are

still, Ah!   Ah!   Ah!   Ah!   Ah!   Ah!   Ah!   Ah!

*)

dim.   *molto rit.*

(MANFICO)
mf

Ah,_____ I have sighed to rest _____ me,   Deep _____ in the qui   et

p

*) This extra measure has been added to bring the ensuing melody in a medium vocal register.

grave! Do not for-get me, let me re-mem-ber'd be; Fare-well, my

(LEONRICO)

love, fare thee well, Leo-no-ra. How__ can I for-get__thee, for my love's long en-dur-ing,

Great - er love than mine,__ thou wilt not find it ex-ist - ing;

(MANRICO)

Ah! in heav'n a-bove, I'll wait, my love, for thee, I'll wait, my love I'll wait thee.

LEONORA

For__ I love thee on - -ly and to thee I'll e'er true be,

Death__ shall yield to love__ and o - pen'd wide shall these gates be;

(MANRICO)

Ah! I'll wait for thee, in heav - en there a - bove, I'll wait for thee, I'll wait for

thee! Leo - no - ra mine!____

Home To Our Mountains

(Il Trovatore)

G. Verdi

Yes, I am grief worn and fain would rest me, But more than grief have

sad dreams op - prest me; Should that dread vi - sion rise in my slum - bers,

Rouse me! its hor - rors then may de - part. Rest thee, O

Moth- - -er! __ I will watch o'er thee, Sleep may re-

store sweet peace to thy heart.

Home to our moun- tains let us re - turn, __ love, There in thy

young days peace had its reign: __ There shall thy sweet __ song fall on my

slum - bers, There shall thy lute make me joy - ous a - gain Rest thee, my

moth — er! kneel-ing be - side thee, I will pour forth my— trou-ba-dour

lay. O sing, and wake now thy sweet lute's soft num bers, Yes I will pour

forth my— trou-ba-dour lay, O sing, and wake now thy sweet lute's soft

Largo

G. F. HANDEL

Andantino

EDWIN H. LEMARE.

Angel's Serenade

G. BRAGA

Tempo I

Palm Branches
(Les Rameaux)

J. FAURE

Funeral March

(From Sonata Op. 35, № 4)

FR. CHOPIN

Kol Nidrei

HEBREW MELODY

Inflammatus
(Stabat Mater)

G. ROSSINI

Maestoso con moto

Andante Religioso

FRANCIS THOME

Hallelujah Chorus
(Messiah)

G.F. HÄNDEL

Allegretto moderato

Bridal March
(LOHENGRIN)

R. WAGNER

The Angelus
(from "Picturesque Scenes")

J. MASSENET

Ave Maria

FR. SCHUBERT

Ave Maria

Bach - Gounod

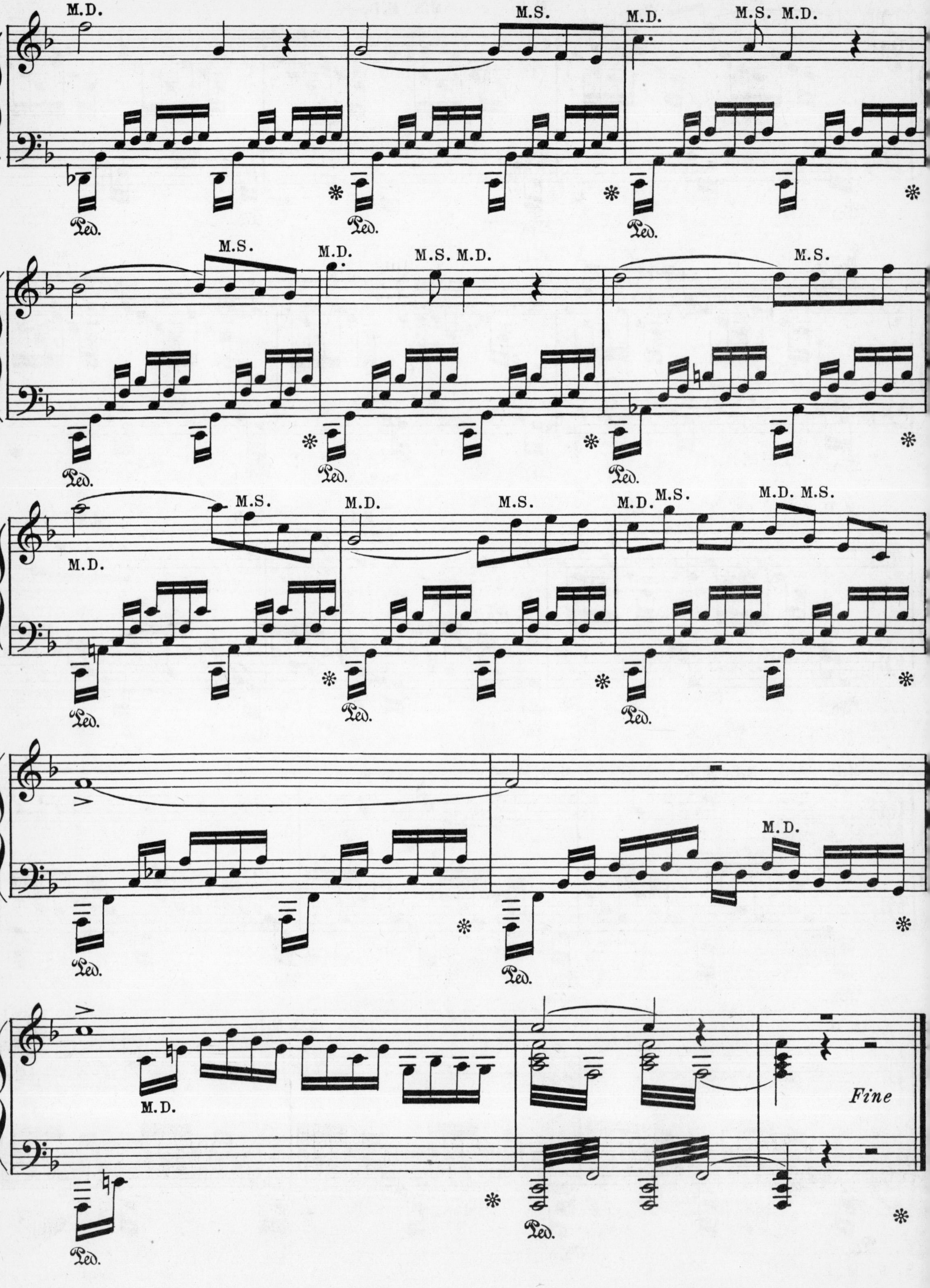
M.D.
M.S.
Ped.
Fine

O Rest In The Lord
(Elijah)

F. MENDELSSOHN

give thee thy heart's de-sires. Com-mit thy way un-to Him, and trust in

Him; com-mit thy way un-to Him, and trust in Him, and fret not thy-

self __ be-cause of e-vil do-ers. O rest in the Lord, wait pa-tient-ly for

Him, wait pa-tient-ly for Him. O rest in the Lord, wait pa-tient-ly for

Ave Maria

BACH-GOUNOD

Calvary

HENRY VAUGHAN

PAUL RODNEY

The pil - grims throng thro' the cit - y gates While the night is fall - ing fast; They go to watch on Cal - v'ry's hill Ere the twi - light hours — are

Giubiloso

Far, far a-way, o'er the dream— of years,— They hear the Voice of the King:—

"Where, O Grave, where is thy vic - to - ry, And where, O Death, is— thy sting?"— Cap - tive He leads them for ev - er - more,—While

Though life may be drear - y, Earth is not thy goal. ___ O lay down thy

bur - den, O come un - to Me, ___ I will not for-sake thee,

I will not for-sake thee, I will not for-sake thee, Though all else should

flee, though all else should flee." ___

Ave Maria
(Adapted from "Cavalleria Rusticana")

Fred. E. Weatherly

P. MASCAGNI

Rock'd In The Cradle Of The Deep

Mrs. Willard

J. P. KNIGHT

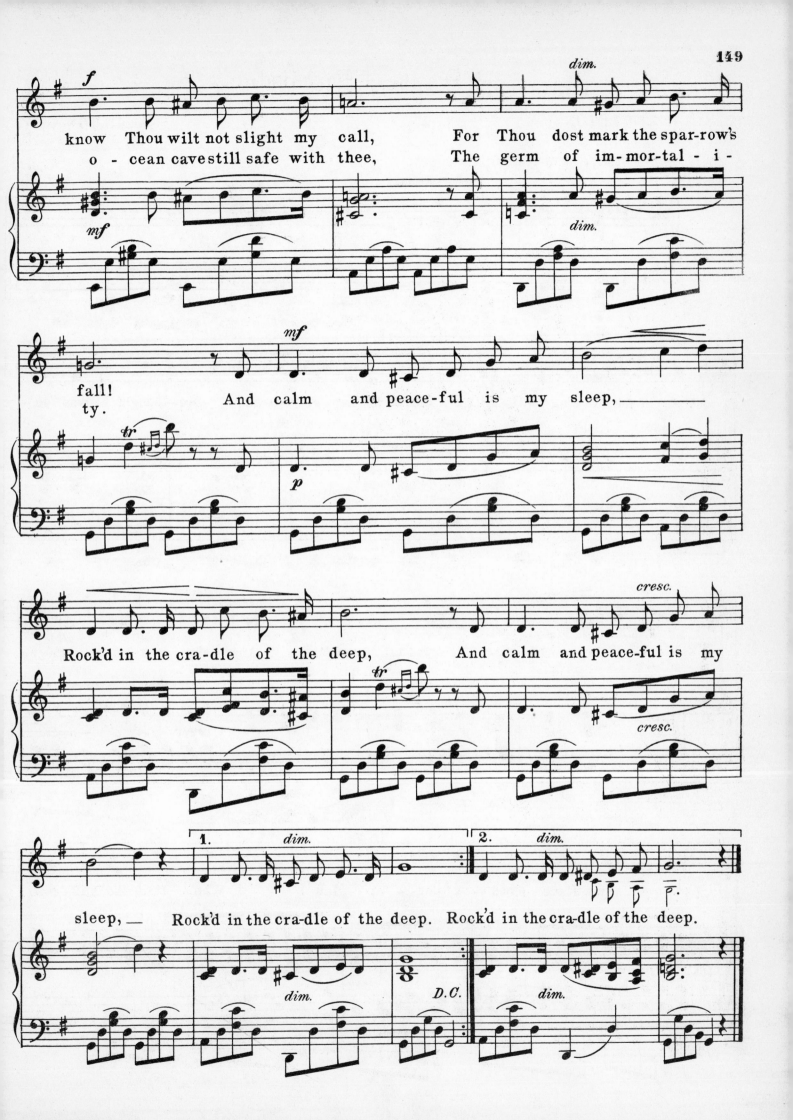

A Dream of Paradise

CLAUDE LITTLETON

HAMILTON GRAY

Andante maestoso

Once in the ev'-ning twi-light, I dreamt a hap-py dream; Me-thought I was in

Heav'n a-bove, And saw its crys-tal gleam. And calm, a-mid the

glo - ry, There stood a sing - er fair, Who thro' the still-ness

poco rit.

colla voce

Ped. assai

song from God's bright an - gel Was sent to make them glad:

Andante grandioso

mf

Fa - ther in Heav'n a-bove, Glo - rious and might - y, Send forth Thy Light of Love,

Ped. ✻ Ped. ✻ *simile*

marcato

O King, most might - y! Fa - ther! Glo - rious and might - y,

rall. **Allegretto**

Send forth Thy Light of Love, Thy Light of Love! And

ff

Ped. ✻ Ped. ✻

154

Hosanna
Easter Song

JULIEN DIDIÉE

JULES GRANIER

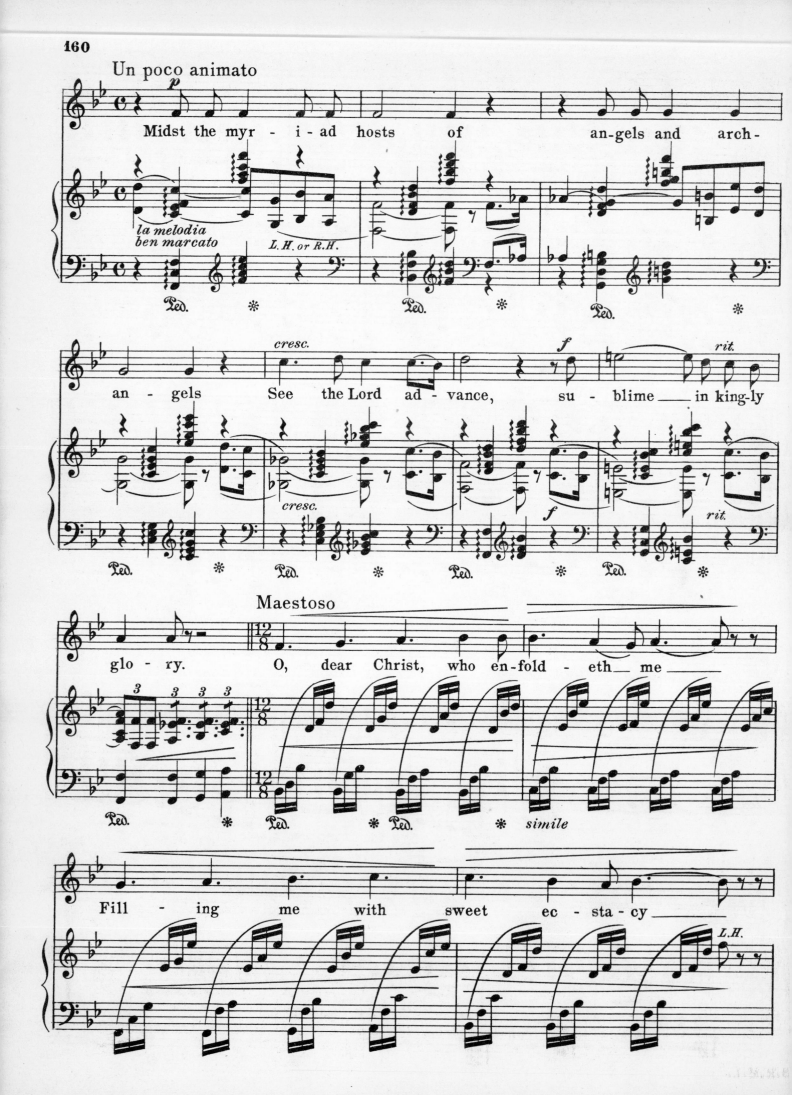

I see thy face __ O, dear Re-deem - er, Ho-

san - na! Ho - san - na! Ho - san - na! praise to

thee! _____ Ho - san - na praise to thee! _____

Jerusalem

NELLA

HENRY PARKER

Maestoso

Piano

"Be-hold, thy King draws near the cit - y gates! Go forth, Je - ru - sa - lem, with shout and song."

And, mov'd as by one thought, the peo-ple rise, And has-ten forth, a glad, tu - mul-tuous throng.

Lord, now as we meet Thee, Sing we Ho - san - na,

Sav - iour, — we greet Thee, Re - deem - er Lord ___ and King ___ Ho -

san - - - - na! Ho -

san - - na.

The Lost Chord

ADELAIDE A. PROCTOR

ARTHUR SULLIVAN

Seat-ed one day at the or-gan, I was wea-ry and ill at ease, And my fin-gers wan-der'd id-ly O-ver the noi-sy keys; I know not what I was play-ing, Or what I was dream-ing then, But I struck one chord of mu-sic, Like the

sound of a great A-men, Like the sound of a great___ A-men.

It flood-ed the crim-son twi-light Like the

close of an An-gel's Psalm And it lay on my fe-ver'd spir-it, With a touch of in-fi-nite

calm, It qui-et-ed pain and sor-row, Like love o-ver-com-ing strife, It

seem'd the har-mo-nious ech-o From our dis-cord-ant life, It link'd all per-plex-ed

mean-ings. In-to one per-fect peace, And trem-bled a-way in-to si-lence As

if it were loth to cease; I have sought, but I seek it vain-ly, That one lost chord di-

vine, Which came from the soul of the or-gan, And en-ter'd in-to mine.

One Sweetly Solemn Thought

R. S. AMBROSE

One sweet-ly sol-emn thought Comes to me o'er and o'er;

I am near-er home to-day Than I've ev-er___ been be-fore. Near_er my Fath-er's house, Where the man_y man-sions be; Near_er the great white throne,_____ Near_er the crys_tal sea;

Near - er the bounds of life, Where we lay our bur - dens

down; Near - er leav - ing the cross,

Near - er___ gain - ing the crown. But ly - ing dark - ly be -

tween,_____ Wind - ing a - down thro' the night,_____

No Shadows Yonder
(Holy City)

A. R. GAUL

No shad-ows yon-der! All light and

song! Each day I won-der and say "How long shall

time me sun-der from that dear throng?" No weep-ing

yon - der! All fled a - way! While here I

wan - der Each wea-ry day, _____ And sigh as I

pon - der my long, long stay. No part-ings

yon - der! Time and space nev - er a - gain____ shall sun - der,

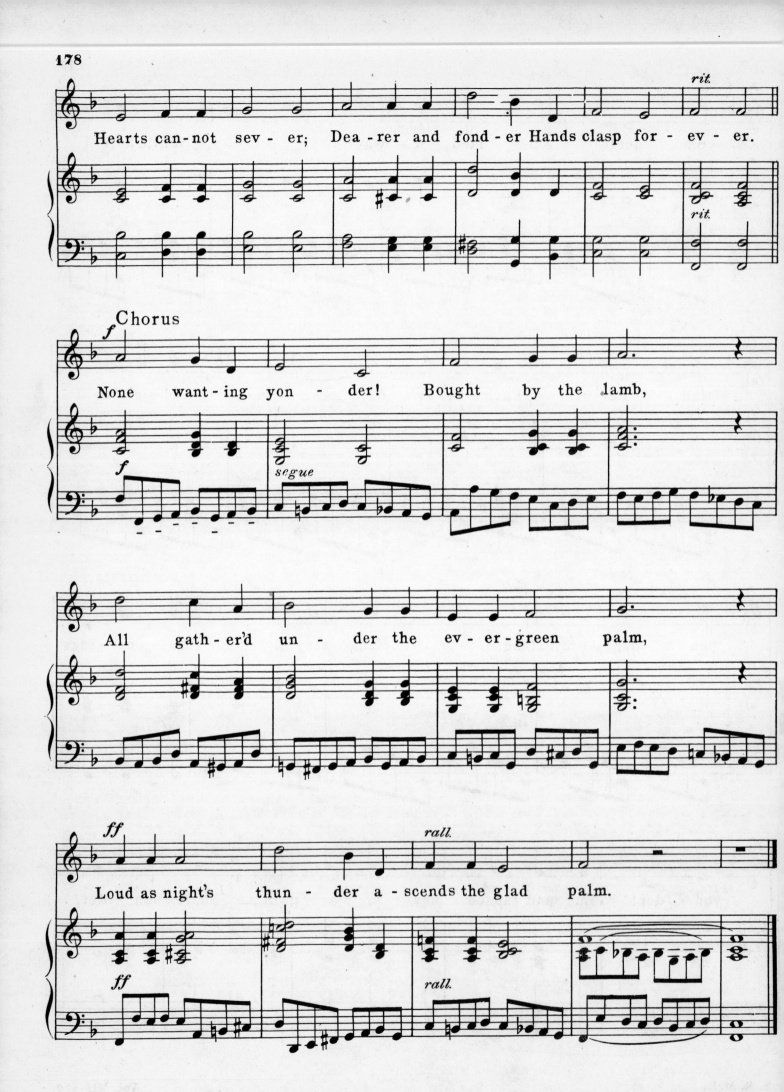

Hearts can-not sev - er; Dea - rer and fond - er Hands clasp for - ev - er.

Chorus

None want-ing yon - der! Bought by the lamb,

All gath - er'd un - der the ev - er-green palm,

Loud as night's thun - der a - scends the glad palm.

The Palms
(Les Rameaux)

J. FAURE

Andante maestoso

1. O'er all the way green palms and blos - soms gay,___
2. His word gave forth and peo - ples by its might,___
3. Sing and re-joice oh blest Je - ru - sa - lem,___

Are strewn this day in fes - tal pre - - pa - ra - tion,
Once more re-gain free-dom from deg - - ra - da - tion,
Of all thy sons sing the e - man - - ci - pa - tion,

Where Je - sus comes to wipe our tears a - way,——
Hu - man - i - ty to each doth give his right,——
Through bound - less love the Christ of Beth - le - hem,——

E'en now the throng to wel - come him pre - pare;
While those in dark - ness find re - stored the light;
Brings faith and hope to thee for ev - er more;

Join all and sing, His name de - clare,

Let ev - 'ry voice re - sound with ac - - cla - ma - tion, Ho-

Over The Stars There Is Rest

T. T. BARKER

FRANZ ABT

Makes the de - light of the blest, _____ Dark, though to - day be with
There are re - lieved the op - prest, _____ On - ward with cour - age re -

sor - row, Hope gilds more bright-ly the mor - row,
viv - ing, Ev - er still pa-tient-ly striv - ing,

O - ver the stars there is rest! _____ O - ver the
O - ver the stars there is rest! _____ O - ver the

stars there is rest! _____
stars there is rest! _____

There Is A Green Hill Far Away

Mrs. C. F. ALEXANDER

CH. GOUNOD

There is a green hill far a-way, With-out a cit-y wall, Where the dear Lord was cru-ci-fied, Who

died to save us all. We may not know, we

can-not tell, What pains He had to bear,

But we be-lieve it was for us He hung and suf-fer'd there. He

died that we might be for-giv'n, He died to make us good,

That we might go at last to heav'n,— Sav'd by His pre-cious blood.

There was no oth - - er good e - nough To

pay the price of sin, He

on - ly could un - lock the gates Of

try ·His works to do.

We must love Him, too!

We must love Him, too, And try His works to

do!

Prayer

"Der Freischütz"

C. M. Von Weber

Soft - ly sighs the voice of _ eve - ning, Steal - ing thro' 'yon shad - y wil - low grove; While the stars, like guard - ian _ an - gels, Set their ho - ly, _ night-ly _ watch a - bove.

Low - ly bend - ing, towards thee wend - ing, Lord, who hast no cause nor end - ing; Still be - friend us, still _ de - fend - ing, Thine e - ter - nal suc - - cor.

Deep River

SPIRITUAL

Crucifixion

SPIRITUAL

Slowly and solemnly

1. They cru - ci - fied my Lord,
2. nailed him to the tree
3. pierced him in the side
4. bowed his head and died

An' he ne-ver said a mum-ba-ling

They cru - ci - fied my Lord,
word; They nailed him to the tree
They pierced him in the side
He bowed his head and died

An' he ne-ver said a mum-ba-ling

1-2-3   4

word, not a word, not a word, not a word

They
They
He

Ev'ry Time I Feel The Spirit

SPIRITUAL

Moderato

mf

1-2-3. Ev-'ry time I feel the Spi-rit mov-in' in my heart, I will

pray. Ev-'ry time I feel the Spi-rit mov-in' in my heart I will

cresc.

pray.
1. 'Pon de moun-tain my Lord spoke, Out His mouth came fire and
2. All a-roun' me look so fine, Ask my Lord if all was
3. Jor-dan ri-ver chil-ly and cold, Chills the bo-dy not the

mf

smoke.
mine.   Ev-'ry time I feel the Spi-rit mov-in' in my heart, I will
soul.

dim.

pray; Ev-'ry time I see the Spi-rit mov-in' in my heart I will pray.

I Couldn't Hear Nobody Pray

SPIRITUAL

pray, _____ I could-n't hear no-bo-dy pray, An' I

could-n't hear no-bo-dy pray, O 'way down yon-der

by my-self An' I could-nt hear no-bo-dy pray.

De Gospel Train

SPIRITUAL

Moderato

mf

1. De gos-pel train am com-in', I hear it jes' at hand, ___ I
2. I hear de bell and whis-tle, A-com-in' round de curve, ___ She's
3. She's near-in' now de sta-tion, O sin-ner, doan' be vain, ___ But

hear dem car-wheels mov-in' An' rum-blin' thro' de land
play-in' all her steam-pow'r An' strain-in' ev-'ry nerve Git on
come and get yo' tick-et Be rea-dy for de train

board, _____ chil-lun, git on board, lit-tle chil-lun, git on board, _____

Chil-lun, there's room for man-y-a more. Git on more.

Little Wheel A-Turnin' In My Heart

SPIRITUAL

Moderato

1. Dere's a lit-tle wheel a-turn-in' in my heart, Dere's a
2. O I feel so ve-ry hap-py in my heart, O I
3. O I don't feel no-ways tir-ed in my heart, O I

lit-tle wheel a-turn-in' in my heart, In my heart, _____ In my
feel so ve-ry hap-py in my heart, In my heart, _____ In my
don't feel no-ways tir-ed in my heart, In my heart, _____ In my

rit. et dim.

heart, _____ Dere's a lit-tle wheel a-turn-in' in my heart
heart, _____ O I feel so ve-ry hap-py in my heart.
heart, _____ O I don't feel no-ways tir-ed in my heart.

Roll, Jordan, Roll

SPIRITUAL

Nobody Knows De Trouble I've Seen

SPIRITUAL

Oh no-bo-dy knows de trou-ble I've seen, No-bo-dy knows but

Je - sus No-bo-dy knows de trou-ble I've seen,

1-*Fine*   2   *mf*

Glo - ry hal-le-lu - jah! Oh lu - jah! Some - times I'm up, some-
though you see me

dim.   *mf*

times I'm down, Oh, yes, Lord. Some - times I'm al - most
goin' 'long so Oh, yes, Lord. I have my tri - als

1   2   *D.C. al Fine*

to the ground,— Oh, yes, Lord. Al -
here be - low,— Oh, yes, Lord.

All God's Chillun Got Wings

SPIRITUAL

I'm A Rolling

SPIRITUAL

I'm a roll - ing, I'm a roll - ing I'm a roll - ing_ thro' an un - friend - ly world, I'm a roll - ing, I'm a roll - ing, thro' an un - friend - ly world!

Fine

O broth - ers, won't you help me?   O broth - ers won't you help me to pray?
O sis - ters, won't you help me   O sis - ters won't you help me to pray?
O preach - ers, won't you help me   O preach - ers won't you help me to pray?

D.S. al Fine

O broth - ers, won't you help me
O sis - ters, won't you help me } Won't you help me in the ser - vice of the Lord I'm a
O preach - ers, won't you help me

Didn't My Lord Deliver Daniel?

SPIRITUAL

Did-n't my Lord de-li-ver Dan-iel, de-li-ver Dan-iel, de-li-ver

Dan-iel? Did-n't my Lord de-li-ver Dan-iel and why not a ev-e-ry

man? He de-li-ver'd Dan-iel from the li-on's den.

I___ set my foot___ on the gos-pel ship, And the

Jo-nah from the bel-ly of the whale, And the He brew chil-dren from the

ship___ it be-gin___ to___ sail, And it land-ed me o-ver on___

fi-ery fur-nace, And___ why not ev-e-ry___ man? Did-n't

Ca-naan's shore, And I'll nev-er come back an-y more.

Somebody's Knockin' At Your Door

SPIRITUAL

Swing Low, Sweet Chariot

SPIRITUAL

Dat Ol'-Time Religion

SPIRITUAL

Keep A-Inching Along

SPIRITUAL

Keep a - inch-ing a-long, Keep a - inch-ing a-long, Mas-sa Je-sus is com-in' bye an'

bye, Keep a - inch-ing a-long like a po' inch worm, Mas-sa Je-sus is com-ing bye an'

bye, O Chris-tians, Keep a bye.

O, I died one time, gwine-ter die no more, Mas-sa
You in de Lord, and de Lord in you, Mas-sa
Can I die when I'm in de Lord, Mas-sa

Je-sus is com-in' bye an' bye. O I died one time gwine-ter
Je-sus is com-in' bye an' bye. O,— you in de Lord and de
Je-sus is com-in' bye an' bye. How can I die when I'm

die — no more, Mas-sa Je-sus is com-in' bye an' bye.
Lord — in you, Mas-sa Je-sus is com-in' bye an' bye.
in — de Lord, Mas-sa Je-sus is com-in' bye an' bye.

D.C. al Fine

Sometimes I Feel Like A Motherless Child

SPIRITUAL

Andante

1. Some-times I feel like a moth-er-less child, Some-times I feel like a
2. Some-times I feel like I'm al - most gone, Some-times I feel like I'm

moth - er - less child; Some-times I feel like a moth - er - less child, A
al - most gone, Some-times I feel like I'm al - most gone, Way

cresc.

long___ ways from home___ A long___ ways_ from home___ A
up___ in de Heav'n - ly land Way up in de Heav-en - ly land___ Way

dim.

long___ ways from home___ A long___ ways_ from home!
up___ in de Heav'n - ly land, Way up in de Heav-en - ly land!

Oh, Wasn't Dat A Wide River?

SPIRITUAL

Moderato

Oh, was-n't that a wide ri - ver, Ri-ver of Jor - dan, Lord, Wide___

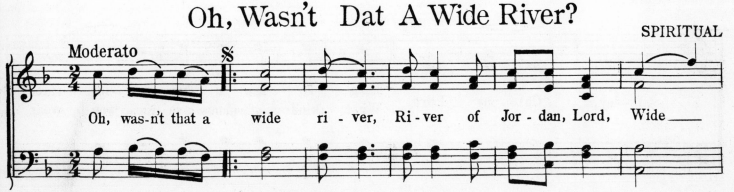

river, Dere's one more ri-ver to cross, Oh, was-n't dat a cross. 1.Oh

you got Je-sus, hold Him fast, One more ri-ver to cross, Oh, bet-ter love was
strong-er than an i-ron band, One more ri-ver to cross, 'Tis sweet-er dan dat

nev-er told,___ One more ri-ver to cross. 2.'Tis
hon-ey comb,___ One more ri-ver to cross. cross. Oh was-n't dat a

D. S. al Fine

He's The Lily Of The Valley

Moderato

He's the li-ly of the val-ley Oh! my Lord; He's the li-ly of the

val-ley, Oh! my Lord. King Je-sus in his char-iot rides,
What kind of shoes are those you wear,

D. S. al Fine

Oh! my Lord, With four white hors-es side by side, Oh! my Lord.
Oh! my Lord, That you can ride up-on the air, Oh! my Lord.

Peter, Go Ring Dem Bells

Lively   SPIRITUAL

Oh, Pe - ter, go ring dem bells, Pe - ter, go___ ring dem bells,

Pe - ter, go ring dem bells, I heard f'om Heav'n to - day! Oh day! I

won-der where my moth-er is gone, I won - der where my moth-er is gone, I
won-der where my sis - ter is gone, I won - der where my sis - ter is gone, I

won-der___ where moth-er is gone, I heard f'om Heav'n to-day.   I
won-der___ where sis-ter is gone, I heard f'om Heav'n to-   day. 0

Steal Away

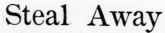

Slowly   cresc. molto   SPIRITUAL

1. Steal a - way, steal a - way, steal a - way to Je - sus!
2. Steal a - way, steal a - way, steal a - way to Je - sus!
3. Steal a - way, steal a - way, steal a - way to Je - sus!

Steal a - way, steal a - way home, I ain't got long_ to stay here!
Steal a - way, steal a - way home, I ain't got long_ to stay here!
Steal a - way, steal a - way home, I ain't got long_ to stay here!

My Lord___ calls me, He calls me by the thun - der,
Green trees are bend - ing, Poor sin - ner stands a trem - blin', The
My Lord___ calls me, He calls me by the light - nin',

trum - pet sounds with in___ my soul, I ain't got long to stay here.

By An' By

Moderato   mf   SPIRITUAL

O, by___ an' by,___ by___ an' by,___ I'm gwine ter lay down my

hea-vy load, O, hea-vy load,___ I know my robes gwine ter fit me well,___
hell is deep an' a dark de spair,___

I'm gwine to lay down my hea-vy load,___ O, hea-vy load,___ I

tried it on at the gates of hell,___ I'm gwine ter lay down my hea-vy load.___ O
stop po' sin-ner an' don't go dere,___

D.S. al Fine

Go Down, Moses

Moderato   SPIRITUAL

1. When Is - rael was in E - gypt's land, Let my peo - ple go!___ Op-
2. "Thus saith the Lord," bold Mo - ses said, Let my peo - ple go!___ If
3. Oh, 'twas a dark and dis - mal night, Let my peo - ple go!___ When

press'd so hard they could not stand, Let my peo - ple go!
not I'll smite your first born dead, Let my peo - ple go! "Go down Mo - ses
Mo - ses led the Is - rael - ites, Let my peo - ple go!

Way down in Egypt's land; Tell ole Pha-raoh to Let my peo-ple go!

Were You There?

Slowly

mp

SPIRITUAL

1. Were you there when they cru - ci - fied my Lord? ___
2. Were you there when they laid him in the tomb? ___

mf   *f*   *dim.*   *ff*

Were you there when they cru - ci - fied my Lord? }
Were you there when they laid him in the tomb? }   Oh! ___

f   *dim.*

Some-times it caus - es me to trem - ble, broth - ers,

p   *rit.*   *p*

trem - ble. Were you there when they cru - ci - fied my Lord?

Hark! Hark! My Soul

VOX ANGELICA

J. B. DYKES

1. Hark! hark, my soul, An - gel - ic songs are swell - ing O'er earths green
2. On - ward we go, for still we hear them sing - ing— "Come, wear - y

fields and o - cean's wave beat shore. How sweet the truth those bless - ed strains are
souls for Je - sus bids you come;" And through the dark, its e - choes sweet - ly

tell - ing Of that new life when sin shall be no more!
ring - ing, The mu - sic of the Gos - pel leads us home.

An - gels of Je - sus, An - gels of light, Sing - ing to wel - come the

pil - grims of the night—Sing - ing to wel - come the pil - grims, the pil - grims of the night.

Work, For The Night Is Coming

LOWELL MASON

There Is A Happy Land

ANDREW YOUNG

Sav - iour King, Loud let His prais - es ring, Praise, praise for aye!
sor - row free, Lord we shall live with Thee, Blest, blest for aye!
King - dom won, And bright a - bove the sun, Reign, reign for aye!

Shall We Gather At The River?

REV. ROBERT LOWRY

1. Shall we gath - er at the riv - er, Where bright an - gel feet have
2. On the mar - gin of the riv - er, Wash - ing up its sil - ver
3. On the bo - som of the riv - er, Where the Sav - iour - King we

trod; With its crys - tal tide for - ev - er Flow - ing from the throne of God?
spray, We shall walk and wor - ship ev - er All the hap - py, gold - en day.
own, We shall meet and sor - row nev - er 'Neath the glo - ry of the throne.

CHORUS

Yes, we'll gath - er at the riv - er, The beau - ti - ful, the beau - ti - ful

riv - er, Gath - er with the saints at the riv - er That flows from the throne of God.

What A Friend We Have In Jesus

JOSEPH SCRIVEN

C. CROZAT CONVERSE

1. What a friend we have in Je - sus, All our sins and griefs to bear;
2. Have we tri - als and temp - ta - tions? Is there trou - ble a - ny - where?
3. Are we weak and heav - y - la - den, Cum - bered with a load of care?

What a priv - i - lege to car - ry Ev - 'ry - thing to God in pray'r.
We should nev - er be dis - cour - aged, Take it to the Lord in pray'r.
Pre - cious Sav - iour still our ref - uge,— Take it to the Lord in pray'r.

Oh, what peace we oft - en for - feit, Oh, what need - less pain we bear—
Can we find a Friend so faith - ful, Who will all our sor - rows share?
Do thy friends de - spise, for - sake thee? Take it to the Lord in pray'r;

All be - cause we do not car - ry Ev - 'ry - thing to God in pray'r.
Je - sus knows our ev - 'ry weak - ness, Take it to the Lord in pray'r.
In His arms 'He'll take and shield thee, Thou wilt find a sol - ace there.

Rock Of Ages

TOPLADY

THOMAS HASTINGS

1. Rock of a - ges, cleft for me, Let me hide my - self in Thee;
2. Could my tears for - ev - er flow, Could my zeal no lan - guor know,
3. While I draw this fleet - ing breath, When my eyes shall close in death,

Let the wa - ter and the blood, From Thy wound - ed side which flowed,
These for sin could not a - tone; Thou must save, and Thou a - lone:
When I rise to worlds un - known, And be - hold Thee on Thy throne,

Be of sin the doub - le cure, Save from wrath and make me pure.
In my hand no price I bring; Sim - ply to Thy cross I cling.
Rock of a - ges, cleft for me, Let me hide my - self in Thee.

One Sweetly Solemn Thought

PHŒBE CARY

C. M. VON WEBER

1. One sweet - ly sol - emn thought Comes to me o'er and o'er; I'm near - er
2. Near - er the bound of life, Where bur - dens are laid down, Near - er to
3. Fa - ther, per - fect my trust; Strengthen the hand of faith To feel Thee,

home to - day Than I have been be - fore; Near - er my Fa - ther's house,
leave the cross, And near - er to the crown: But there lies dark be - tween
when I stand Up - on the shore of death. Be near me when my feet

Where ma - ny man - sions be; Near - er the great white throne, Near - er the crys - tal sea.
And wind - ing through the night, The deep and un - known stream That leads at last to light.
Are wait - ing on the brink! I may be near - er home, Near - er than now I think!

Rest For The Weary

S.Y. HARMER

WILLIAM McDONALD

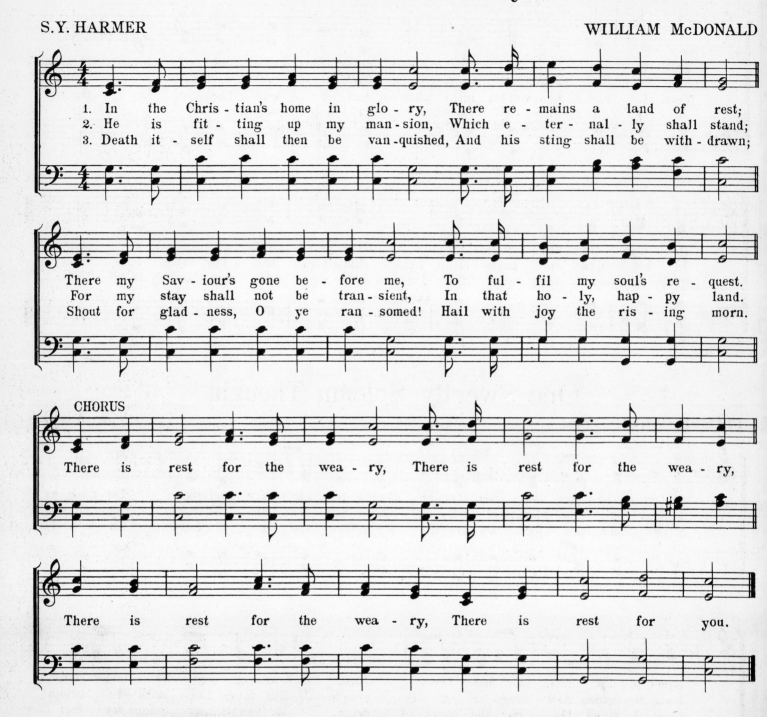

1. In the Chris-tian's home in glo-ry, There re-mains a land of rest;
2. He is fit-ting up my man-sion, Which e-ter-nal-ly shall stand;
3. Death it-self shall then be van-quished, And his sting shall be with-drawn;

There my Sav-iour's gone be-fore me, To ful-fil my soul's re-quest.
For my stay shall not be tran-sient, In that ho-ly, hap-py land.
Shout for glad-ness, O ye ran-somed! Hail with joy the ris-ing morn.

CHORUS

There is rest for the wea-ry, There is rest for the wea-ry,

There is rest for the wea-ry, There is rest for you.

While Shepherds Watched Their Flocks

W. TANSUR

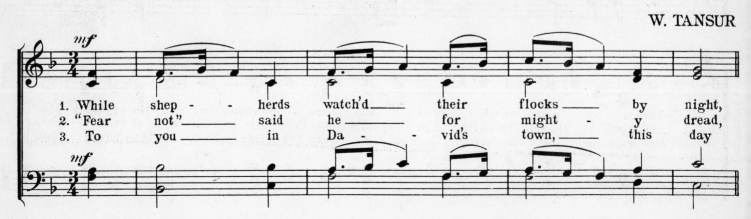

1. While shep - - herds watch'd____ their flocks ____ by night,
2. "Fear not"____ said he ____ for might - y dread,
3. To you ____ in Da - vid's town,____ this day

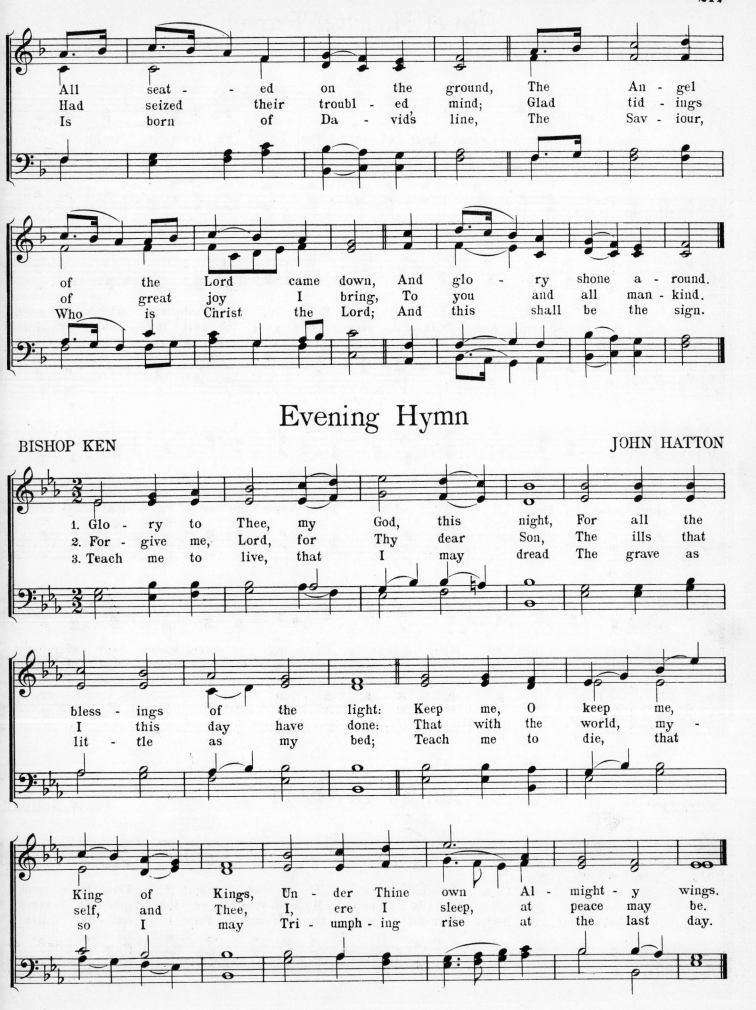

All seat - - ed on the ground, The An - gel
Had seized their troubl - ed mind; Glad tid - ings
Is born of Da - vid's line, The Sav - iour,

of the Lord came down, And glo - ry shone a - round.
of great joy I bring, To you and all man - kind.
Who is Christ the Lord; And this shall be the sign.

Evening Hymn

BISHOP KEN   JOHN HATTON

1. Glo - ry to Thee, my God, this night, For all the
2. For - give me, Lord, for Thy dear Son, The ills that
3. Teach me to live, that I may dread The grave as

bless - ings of the light: Keep me, O keep me,
I this day have done: That with the world, my -
lit - tle as my bed; Teach me to die, that

King of Kings, Un - der Thine own Al - might - y wings.
self, and Thee, I, ere I sleep, at peace may be.
so I may Tri - umph - ing rise at the last day.

Sweet Hour Of Prayer

WM. W. WALFORD

W. B. BRADBURY

Sweet hour of prayer! sweet hour of prayer! That calls me from a world of care,
Sweet hour of prayer! sweet hour of prayer! Thy wings shall my pe - ti - tion bear
Sweet hour of prayer! sweet hour of prayer! May I thy con - so - la - tion share,

And bids me at my Fa - ther's throne Make all my wants and wish - es known:
To Him whose truth and faith - ful - ness En - gage the wait - ing soul to bless.
Till, from Mount Pis - gah's loft - y height, I view my home and take my flight;

In sea - sons of dis - tress and grief, My soul has oft - en found re - lief;
And since He bids me seek His face, Be - lieve His word, and trust His grace,
This robe of flesh I'll drop, and rise To seize the ev - er - last - ing prize;

And oft es - caped the temp - ter's snare, By thy re - turn, sweet hour of prayer!
I'll cast on Him my ev - 'ry care And wait for thee, sweet hour of prayer!
And shout, while pass - ing through the air, Fare - well, fare - well, sweet hour of prayer!

Sun Of My Soul

HURSLEY

W. H. MONK

Sun of my soul, Thou Sav - iour dear, It is not night if Thou be near;
When the soft dews of kind - ly sleep My wea - ried eye - lids gen - tly steep,
A - bide with me from morn till eve, For with - out Thee I can - not live;

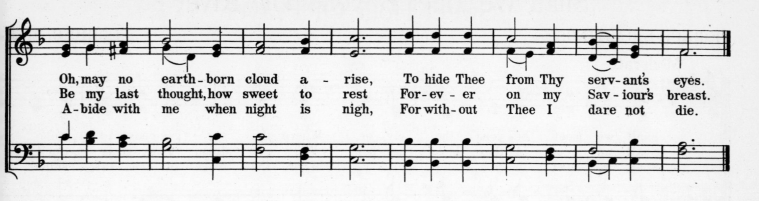

Oh, may no earth-born cloud a - rise, To hide Thee from Thy serv-ant's eyes.
Be my last thought, how sweet to rest For-ev - er on my Sav-iour's breast.
A-bide with me when night is nigh, For with-out Thee I dare not die.

The Son Of God Goes Forth To War

ALL SAINTS   HENRY S. CUTLER

The Son of God goes forth to war, A king - ly crown to gain;___
That mar - tyr first whose ea - gle eye Could pierce be - yond the grave;___
A no - ble band, the chos - en few On whom the Spir - it came,___

His blood - red ban - ner streams a - far: Who fol - lows in His train?
Who saw his Mas - ter in the sky, And called on Him to save;
Twelve val - iant saints, their hope they knew And mocked the torch of flame;

Who best can drink his cup of woe, Tri - um - phant o - ver pain?___
Like Him with par - don on His tongue, In midst of mor - tal pain,___
They met the ty - rant's bran - dished steel, The li - on's gor - y mane,___

Who pa - tient bears his cross be - low, He fol - lows in His train.
He pray'd for them that did the wrong: Who fol - lows in His train?
They bowed their necks the stroke to feel: Who fol - lows in their train?

Shall We Meet Beyond The River?

HORACE L. HASTINGS

ELIHU S. RICE

Moderato

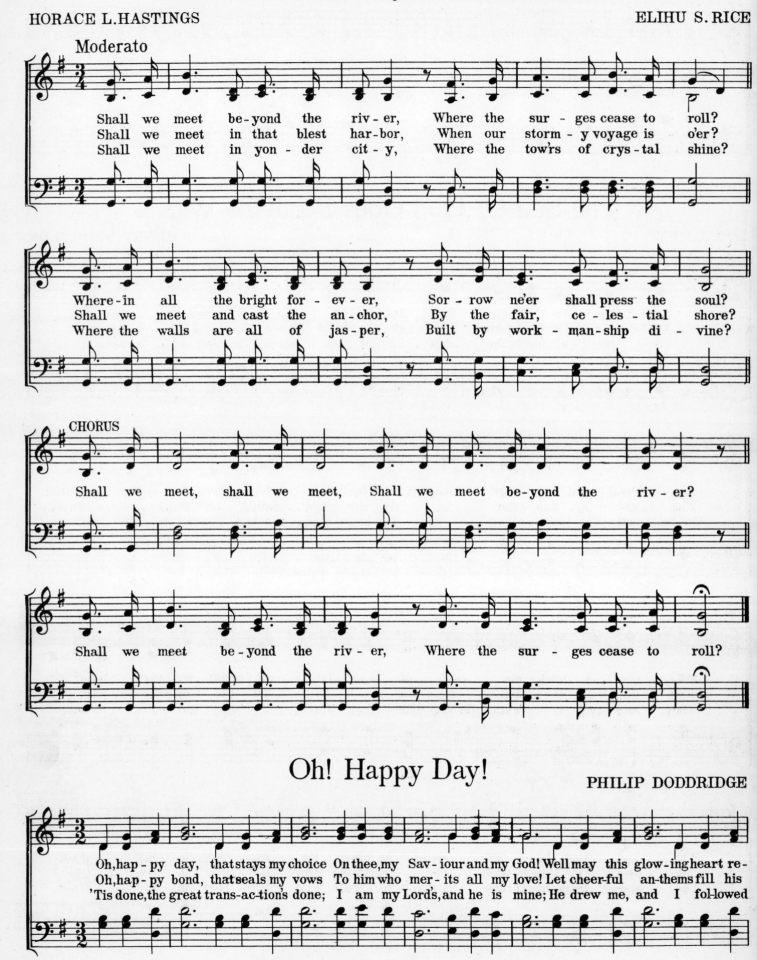

Shall we meet be-yond the riv-er, Where the sur-ges cease to roll?
Shall we meet in that blest har-bor, When our storm-y voyage is o'er?
Shall we meet in yon-der cit-y, Where the tow'rs of crys-tal shine?

Where-in all the bright for-ev-er, Sor-row ne'er shall press the soul?
Shall we meet and cast the an-chor, By the fair, ce-les-tial shore?
Where the walls are all of jas-per, Built by work-man-ship di-vine?

CHORUS

Shall we meet, shall we meet, Shall we meet be-yond the riv-er?

Shall we meet be-yond the riv-er, Where the sur-ges cease to roll?

Oh! Happy Day!

PHILIP DODDRIDGE

Oh, hap-py day, that stays my choice On thee, my Sav-iour and my God! Well may this glow-ing heart re-
Oh, hap-py bond, that seals my vows To him who mer-its all my love! Let cheer-ful an-thems fill his
'Tis done, the great trans-ac-tion's done; I am my Lord's, and he is mine; He drew me, and I fol-lowed

§ CHORUS.

joice, And tell its rap - tures all a - broad.
house, While to that sa - cred shrine I move.
on, Charmed to con - fess the voice di - vine.

Hap - py day, hap - py day, When Je - sus

Fine.

D.S.

washed my sins a - way! He taught me how to watch and pray, And live re - joic - ing ev - 'ry day.

Nearer, My God, To Thee

BETHANY

LOWELL MASON

Near - er, my God, to Thee, Near - er to Thee!— E'en tho' it
Tho' like the wan - der - er, The sun gone down,— Dark - ness be
Then with my wak - ing tho'th Bright with Thy praise,— Out of my

be a cross That rais - eth me, — Still all my song shall be,
o - ver me, My rest a stone;— Yet in my dreams I'd be,
sto - ny griefs Beth - el I'll raise;— So by my woes to be,

Near - er, my God, to Thee, Near - er, my God, to Thee, Near - er to Thee!—
Near - er, my God, to Thee, Near - er, my God, to Thee, Near - er to Thee!—
Near - er, my God, to Thee, Near - er, my God, to Thee, Near - er to Thee!—

O Paradise!

J. BARNBY

PARADISE

♩ = 92 *mf*

O Par - a - dise! O Par - a - dise! Who doth not crave for rest?
O Par - a, - dise! O Par - a - dise! The world is grow - ing old;
O Par - a - dise! O Par - a - dise! We long to sin no more,

Who would not seek the hap - py land Where they that loved are blest;
Who would not be at rest and free Where love is nev - er cold?
We long to be as pure on earth As on thy spot - less shore;

Where loy - al hearts and true,
Where loy - - al hearts and true, Stand ev - er in the light,

All rap - ture, thro' and thro', In God's most. ho - ly sight.

Softly Now The Light Of Day

WEBER

C. M. VON WEBER

Soft - ly now the light of day Fades up - on my sight a - way;
Thou, whose all - per - vad - ing eye Naught es - capes, with - out, with - in,
Soon for me the light of day Shall for - ev - er pass a - way;

Free from care, from la - bor free, Lord, I would com - mune with Thee.
Par - don each in - firm - i - ty, O - pen fault and se - cret sin.
Then, from sin and sor - row free, Take me, Lord, to dwell with Thee.

Onward, Christian Soldiers

ST. GERTRUDE

A. S. SULLIVAN

On - ward, Chris - tian sol - diers, March - ing as to war, With the cross of Je - sus
Like a might - y ar - my, Moves the Church of God; Broth - ers, we are tread - ing
Crowns and thrones may per - ish, King - doms rise and wane, But the Church of Je - sus

Go - ing on be - fore. Christ, the roy - al Mas - ter, Leads a - gainst the foe;
Where the saints have trod; We are not di - vid - ed All one bod - y we,
Con - stant will re - main; Gates of hell can nev - er 'Gainst that church pre - vail,

CHORUS.

For - ward in - to bat - tle, See, His ban - ners go.
One in hope and doc - trine, One in char - i - ty. On - ward, Chris - tian sol - diers,
We have Christ's own prom - ise And that can - not fail.

March - ing as to war, With the cross of Je - sus Go - ing on be - fore.

O Jesus, Thou Art Standing

JUSTIN H. KNECHT

ST. EDITH

1. O Je - sus, Thou art stand - ing Out - side the fast - closed door,
2. O Je - sus, Thou art knock - ing And lo! that hand is scarr'd,
3. O Je - sus, Thou art plead - ing In ac - cents meek and low,

In low - ly pa - tience wait - ing To pass the thresh - old o'er;
And thorns Thy brow en - cir - cle, And tears Thy face have marr'd.
"I died for you, My chil - dren, And will ye treat me so?"

We bear the name of Chris - tians, His name and sign we bear:
O love that pass - eth know - ledge, So pa - tient - ly to wait!
O Lord, with shame and sor - row We o - pen now the door,

O shame, thrice shame up - on us, To keep Him stand - ing there!
O sin that hath no e - qual, So fast to bar the gate!
Dear Sav - iour, en - ter, en - ter, And leave us nev - er - more.

Jesus Lives!

ST. ALBINUS

H. J. GAUNTLETT

mf

1. Je - sus lives! Thy ter - rors now, Can no long - er,
2. Je - sus lives! hence - forth is death But the gate of
3. Je - sus lives! for us He died; Then a - lone to

death, ap - pal us Je - sus lives! by this we know
life im - mor - tal; This shall calm our trem - bling breath,
Je - sus liv - ing Pure in heart may we a - bide,

Thou, O grave, canst not en - thral us.
When we pass its gloom - y por - tal. Al - le - lu - ia.
Glo - ry to our Sav - iour giv - ing.

I Need Thee Every Hour

NEED

ROBERT LOWRY

1. I need Thee ev - 'ry hour, Most gra - cious Lord! No ten - der voice like
2. I need Thee ev - 'ry hour, Stay Thou near by; Temp - ta - tions lose their
3. I need Thee ev - 'ry hour, In joy or pain: Come quick - ly and a -

REFRAIN

Thine Can peace af - ford.
pow'r When Thou art nigh. I need Thee, oh! I need Thee, Ev - 'ry hour I
bide, Or life is vain.

need Thee; Oh! bless me now, my Sav - iour! I come to Thee.

The Ninety And Nine

E. C. CLEPHANE

IRA D. SANKEY

There were ninety and nine, that safe-ly lay In the shel-ter of the fold,
"Lord,— Thou hast here Thy nine-ty and nine, Are they not e-nough for Thee?"
But none of the ran-somed ev-er knew How deep were the wa-ters crossed;

But one was out on the hills a-way, Far off from the gates of gold
But the Shep-herd made an-swer: "This of mine Has wan-dered a-way from me,
Nor how dark was the night that the Lord passed thro' Ere He found His sheep that was lost.

A-way on the moun-tains wild and bare, A-way from the ten-der
And al-though the road be rough and steep, I go to the des-ert to
Out in the des-ert He heard its cry Sick and help-less, and

Shep-herd's care, A-way from the ten-der Shep-herd's care.
find my sheep, I go to the des-ert to find my sheep."
read-y to die, Sick and help-less, and read-y to die.

Copyright 1904 by Ira D. Sankey

Renewal. Used by permission

Pleyel's Hymn.

IGNAZ PLEYEL.

Gra-cious Spir-it, Love di-vine, Let Thy light with-in me shine;
Life and peace to me im-part, Seal sal-va-tion on my heart:
Let me nev-er from Thee stray, Keep me in the nar-row way;

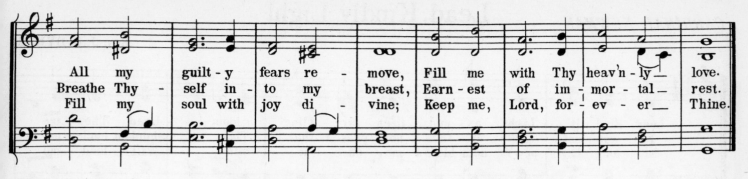

All my guilt-y fears re - move, Fill me with Thy heav'n-ly love.
Breathe Thy - self in - to my breast, Earn - est of im - mor - tal rest.
Fill my soul with joy di - vine; Keep me, Lord, for - ev - er Thine.

A Mighty Fortress Is Our God

MARTIN LUTHER

A might-y fort-ress is our God, A bul-wark nev-er fail - ing:
Did we in our own strength con - fide, Our striv-ing would be los - ing;
And though this world, with dev-ils filled, Should threat-en to un - do us;

Our Help-er He, a - mid the flood Of mor-tal ills pre - vail - ing.
Were not the right man on our side, The man of God's own choos - ing.
We will not fear, for God hath willed His truth to tri - umph through us.

For still our an - cient foe Doth seek to work us woe; His craft and pow'r are great,
Dost ask who that may be? Christ Je - sus, it is He; Lord Sab - aoth is His name,
The prince of dark - ness grim, We trem-ble not for him; His rage we can en - dure,

And armed with cru - el hate, On earth is not his e - qual.
From age to age the same, And He must win the bat - tle.
For lo! his doom is sure, One lit - tle word shall fell him.

Lead, Kindly Light

CARDINAL NEWMAN

Rev. J. B. DYKES

Lead, Kind-ly Light, a-mid th'en-cir-cling gloom Lead Thou me
I was not ev-er thus nor prayed that Thou Shouldst lead me
So long Thy pow'r hath bless'd me, sure it still Will lead me

on; The night is dark and I am far from home, Lead Thou me
on; I loved to choose and see my path, but now Lead Thou me
on; O'er moor and fen, o'er crag and tor-rent, till The night is

on. Keep Thou my feet, I do not ask to see
on. I loved the gar-ish day, and, spite of fears
gone And with the morn those an-gel fa-ces smile

The dis-tant scene; one step e-nough for me.
Pride ruled my will: re-mem-ber not past years.
Which I have loved long since, and lost a-while.

Old Hundred

OLD HUNDREDTH

L. BOURGEOIS

All peo-ple that on earth do dwell, Sing to the Lord with cheer-ful voice,
Know that the Lord is God in-deed; With-out our aid He did us make:
Praise God, from whom all bless-ings flow, Praise Him, all crea-tures here be-low;

Him serve with mirth, His praise forth tell, Come ye be-fore Him and re-joice.
We are His flock, He doth us feed, And for His sheep He doth us take.
Praise Him a-bove, ye heav'n-ly host; Praise Fa-ther, Son, and Ho-ly Ghost.

Joy To The World

ISAAK WATTS.

G. F. HANDEL.

Joy to the world, the Lord has come; Let earth re-ceive her King. Let
Joy to the earth, the Sav-iour reigns; Let men their songs em-ploy; While
No more let sin and sor-row grow, Nor thorns in-fest the ground; He

ev-'ry heart pre-pare Him room, And heav'n and na-ture sing, And
fields and floods, rocks, hills and plains, Re-peat the sound-ing joy, Re-
comes to make His bless-ings flow, Far as the course is found, Far

And heav'n and na-ture
Re-peat the sound-ing
Far as the course is

heav'n and na-ture sing, And heav'n, and heav'n and na-ture sing.
peat the sound-ing joy, Re-peat, re-peat the sound-ing joy.
as the course is found, Far as the course, the course is found.

sing, And heav'n and na-ture sing,
joy, Re-peat the sound-ing joy,
found, Far as the course is found,

Jesus, Lover Of My Soul

CHARLES WESLEY

S. B. MARSH

Reverently

1. Je - sus, lov - er of my soul, Let me to Thy bo - som fly,—
2. Oth - er ref - uge have I none; Hangs my help - less soul on Thee;
3. Plen-teous grace with Thee is found, Grace to cov - er all my sin;—

While the near - er wa - ters roll, While the tem - pest still is high,—
Leave, ah! leave me not a - lone, Still sup - port and com - fort me!—
Let the heal - ing streams a - bound; Make and keep me pure with - in!—

Hide me, O my Sav - iour! hide, Till the storm of life be past;
All my trust on Thee is stayed, All my help from Thee I bring;
Thou of life the Foun - tain art, Free - ly let me take of Thee;

Safe in - to the ha - ven guide; Oh! re - ceive my soul at last!
Cov - er my de - fence - less head With the shad - ow of Thy wing!
Spring Thou up with - in my heart! Rise to all e - ter - ni - ty!—

O God, Our Help In Ages Past

ST. ANNE

WILLIAM CROFT

1. O God, our help in a - ges past, Our hope for years to come,
2. Be - fore the hills in or - der stood, Or earth re - ceived her frame,
3. A thou-sand a - ges in Thy sight Are like an eve - ning gone;

Our shel - ter from the storm - y blast, And our e - ter - nal home!
From ev - er - last - ing Thou art God, To end - less years the same.
Short as the watch that ends the night Be - fore the ris - ing sun.

Jerusalem The Golden

EWING

ALEX EWING

1. Je - ru - sa - lem the gold - en, With milk and hon - ey blest,
2. They stand, those halls of Zi - on, All ju - bi - lant with song,
3. There is the throne of Da - vid, And there from care re - leased,

Be - neath thy con - tem - pla - tion Sink heart and voice op - prest.
And bright with many an an - gel, And all the mar - tyr throng.
The song of them that tri - umph, The shout of them that feast;

I know not, Oh, I know not, What joys a - wait us there,
The Prince is ev - er in them, The day light is se - rene;
And they who with their Lead - er Have con - quered in the fight,

What ra - dian - cy of glo - ry, What bliss be - yond com - pare.
The pas - tures of the bless - ed Are decked in glo - rious sheen.
For - ev - er and for - ev - er Are clad in robes of white.

In Heavenly Love Abiding

Andante, non lento

FELIX MENDELSSOHN

1. In heav'n-ly love a - bi - ding, No change my heart shall fear, And safe in such con-
2. Wher - ev - er He may guide me, No want shall turn me back; My Shep-herd is be-
3. Green past-ures are be - fore me, Which yet I have not seen, Bright skies will soon be

fid - ing, For noth - ing chang - es here. The storm may roar with - out me
side me, And noth - ing can I lack. His wis - dom ev - er wak - eth,
o'er me, Where dark - est clouds have been. My hope I can - not meas - ure,

My heart may low be laid, But God is round a - bout me, And can I be dis-
His sight is nev - er dim; He knows the way He tak - eth, And I will walk with
My path to life is free, My Sav - iour has my treas-ure, And He will walk with

mayed? But God is round a - bout me, And can I be dis - mayed?
Him; He knows the way He tak - eth And I will walk with Him.
me; My Sav - iour has my treas - ure, And He will walk with me.

Holy Night! Peaceful Night!

J. MOHR

FRANZ GRUBER

1. Ho - ly night! peace - ful night! Thro' the dark - ness beams a light,
2. Si - lent night! ho - li - est night! Dark - ness flies and all is light!
3. Si - lent night! ho - li - est night! Guid - ing Star, O lend thy light!

Yon - der, where they sweet vig - ils keep, O'er the Babe, who in si - lent sleep,
Shep-herds hear the an - gels sing: "Hal - le - lu - jah! hail the King!
See the east - ern wise men bring Gifts and hom - age to our King!

Rallentando.

Rests in heav - en - ly peace, Rests in heav - en - ly peace.__
Je - sus the Sav - iour is here! Je - sus the Sav - iour is here!"__
Je - sus the Sav - iour is here! Je - sus the Sav - iour is here!__

I'm A Pilgrim

MARY S.B. DANA

1. I'm a pil - grim, and I'm a stran-ger: I can tar - ry, I can tar - ry but a night.
2. Of that coun - try to which I'm go - ing, My Re - deem-er, my Re - deem-er is the light:
3. There the sun - beams are ev - er shin - ing, And I'm long-ing, I am long-ing for the sight;

Do not de - tain me, for I am go - ing To where the stream-lets are ev - er flow-ing.
There is no sor - row, nor an - y sigh - ing, Nor an - y sin there, nor an - y dy - ing.
With - in a coun - try, un-known and drear - y, I have been wand'-ring, for-lorn and wea - ry.

Refrain

I'm a pil - grim, and I'm a stran - ger: I can tar - ry, I can tar - ry but a night.

Carol, Carol, Christians

A. CLEVELAND COXE

Semi Chorus

Car-ol, Car-ol, Christians! Car-ol joy-ful-ly— Car-ol for the com-ing of Christ's na-ti-vi-ty.

Chorus(forte) Animated   unison

Car-ol, Car-ol, Chris-tians! Car-ol joy-ful-ly— Car-ol for the com-ing of Christ's na-ti-vi-ty; And

pray a glad-some Christmas, For all good Christian men. Car-ol, Car-ol, Chris-tians! For Christmas come a-gain.

Fine.

Semi Chorus

1. Go ye to the for-est, Where the myr-tles grow, Where the pine and
2. Wreathe your Christ-mas gar-land Where to Christ we pray; It shall smell like
3. Car-ol, Car-ol Chris-tians! Like the Ma-gi, now, Ye must lade your

lau-rel bend be-neath the snow; Gath-er them for Je-sus,
Car-mel on our fes-tal day. Lib-an-us and Sha-ron,
cask-ets with a grate-ful vow; Ye must have sweet in-cense,

Wreathe them for His shrine; Make His tem - ple glo - rious With the box and pine.
Shall not green-er be Than our ho - ly chan - cel, On Christ's na - ti - vi - ty.
Myrrh and fin-est gold, At our Christ-mas al - tar, Hum - bly to un - fold.

D.C. Chorus.

It Came Upon The Midnight Clear

CAROL   R. S. WILLIS

1. It came up - on the mid - night clear, That glo - rious song of old,—
2. Still through the clo - ven skies they come, With peace - ful wings un - furled;
3. And ye be - neath life's crush - ing load, Whose forms are bend - ing low,—

From an - gels bend - ing near the earth, To touch their harps of gold:—
And still their heaven - ly mu - sic floats O'er all the wea - ry world.
Who toil a - long the climb - ing way With pain - ful steps and slow;—

"Peace to the earth, good - will to men, From heaven's all gra - cious King;"—
A - bove its sad and low - ly plains They bend on hover - ing wing,—
Look now! for glad and gold - en hours Come swift - ly on the wing;—

The world in sol - emn still - ness lay, To hear the an - gels sing!—
And ev - er o'er its Ba - bel sounds, The bless - ed an - gels sing!—
Oh, rest be - side the wea - ry road, And hear the an - gels sing!—

How Firm A Foundation

R. KEENE

1. How firm a foun-da-tion, ye saints of the Lord, Is laid for your
2. Fear not, I am with thee, O, be not dis-mayed, For I am thy
3. When thro' the deep wa-ters I call thee to go, The riv-ers of

faith in His ex-cel-lent Word! What more can He say than to
God, I will still give thee aid: I'll strength-en thee help thee, and
woe shall not thee o-ver-flow; For I will be with thee thy

you He hath said You who un-to Je-sus for ref-uge have
cause thee to stand, Up-held by My right-eous, om-ni-po-tent
trou-ble to bless, And sanc-ti-fy to thee thy deep-est dis-

fled? You who un-to Je-sus for ref-uge have fled?
Hand, Up-held by My right-eous, om-ni-po-tent Hand.
tress And sanc-ti-fy to thee thy deep-est dis-tress.

Now The Day Is Over

MERRIAL

I. BARNBY

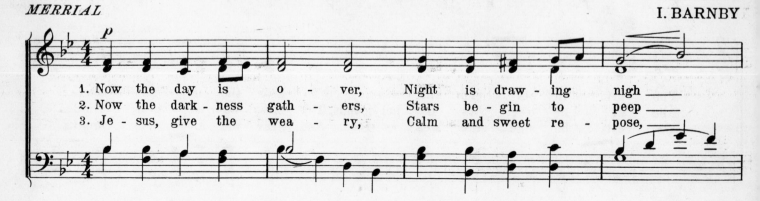

1. Now the day is o-ver, Night is draw-ing nigh
2. Now the dark-ness gath-ers, Stars be-gin to peep
3. Je-sus, give the wea-ry, Calm and sweet re-pose,

Shad - ows of the ev' - ning Steal a - cross the sky.
Birds and beasts and flow - ers Soon will be a - sleep.
With Thy ten - d'rest bless - ing May our eye - lids close.

Holy! Holy! Lord God Almighty!

NICAEA

JOHN B. DYKES

1. Ho - ly, Ho - ly, Ho - ly, Lord God al - might - y!
2. Ho - ly, Ho - ly, Ho - ly, all the saints a - dore Thee,
3. Ho - ly, Ho - ly, Ho - ly, tho' the dark - ness hide Thee,

Ear - ly in the morn - ing our song shall rise to Thee;
Cast - ing down their gold - en crowns a - round the glass - y sea;
Tho' the eye of sin - ful man Thy glo - ry may not see;

Ho - ly, Ho - ly, Ho - ly! Mer - ci - ful and Might - y!
Cher - u - bim and Ser - a - phim fall - ing down be - fore Thee,
On - ly Thou art Ho - ly there is none be - side Thee,

God in three Per - sons, bless - ed Trin - i - ty!
Which wert and art, and ev - er - more shall be.
Per - fect in pow'r, in love, and pur - i - ty.

Heav'n Is My Home

A. SULLIVAN

1. I'm but a strang-er here, Heav'n is my home;
2. What though the tem-pest rage, Heav'n is my home;
3. There-fore, I mur-mur not, Heav'n is my home;

Earth is a des-ert drear, Heav'n is my home.
Short is my pil-gri-mage, Heav'n is my home.
What-e'er my earth-ly lot, Heav'n is my home.

Dan-ger and sor-row stand Round me on ev'-ry hand,
And time's wild wint-'ry blast Soon will be ov-er past,
And I shall sure-ly stand There, at my Lord's right hand;

Heav'n is my Fa-ther-land,— Heav'n is my home.
I shall reach home at last,— Heav'n is my home.
Heav'n is my Fa-ther-land,— Heav'n is my home.

Children's Hosanna

JOHN KING

GEO. J. WEBB

1. When His sal-va-tion bring-ing, To Zi-on Je-sus came, The chil-dren all stood
2. And since the Lord re-tain-eth His love for chil-dren still— Tho' now as King he
3. For should we fail pro-claim-ing Our great Re-deem-ers praise, The stones, our si-lence

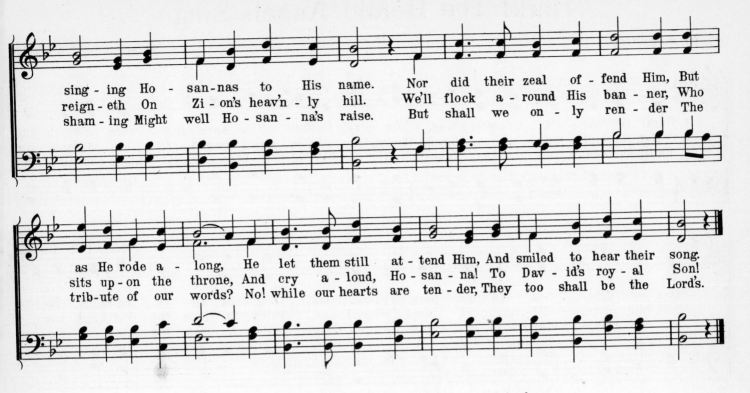

sing - ing Ho - san-nas to His name. Nor did their zeal of - fend Him, But
reign - eth On Zi - on's heav'n - ly hill. We'll flock a - round His ban - ner, Who
sham - ing Might well Ho - san - na's raise. But shall we on - ly ren - der The

as He rode a - long, He let them still at - tend Him, And smiled to hear their song.
sits up - on the throne, And cry a - loud, Ho - san - na! To Dav - id's roy - al Son!
trib - ute of our words? No! while our hearts are ten - der, They too shall be the Lord's.

The Church's One Foundation

SAMUEL I. STONE

S. S. WESLEY

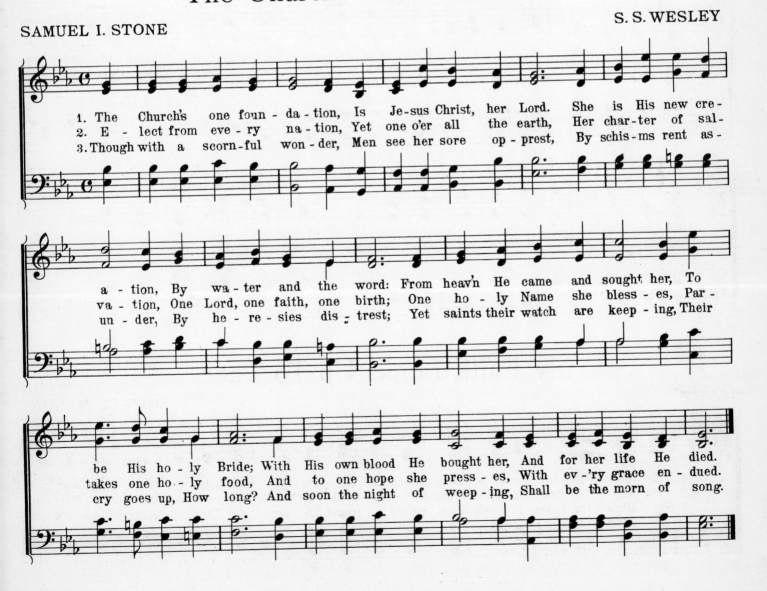

1. The Church's one foun - da - tion, Is Je - sus Christ, her Lord. She is His new cre -
2. E - lect from eve - ry na - tion, Yet one o'er all the earth, Her char - ter of sal -
3. Though with a scorn - ful won - der, Men see her sore op - prest, By schis - ms rent as -

a - tion, By wa - ter and the word: From heav'n He came and sought her, To
va - tion, One Lord, one faith, one birth; One ho - ly Name she bless - es, Par -
un - der, By he - re - sies dis - trest; Yet saints their watch are keep - ing, Their

be His ho - ly Bride; With His own blood He bought her, And for her life He died.
takes one ho - ly food, And to one hope she press - es, With ev - 'ry grace en - dued.
cry goes up, How long? And soon the night of weep - ing, Shall be the morn of song.

Hark! The Herald Angels Sing

MENDELSSOHN

F. MENDELSSOHN

1. Hark! the her - ald an - gels sing, "Glo - ry to the new - born King! Peace on earth, and
2. Christ, by high - est heav'n a - dored; Christ, the ev - er - last - ing Lord; Late in time be -
3. Hail! the heav'n-born Prince of peace! Hail! the Son of Right-eous-ness! Light and life to

mer - cy mild, God and sin - ners re - con - ciled." Joy - ful, all ye na - tions rise,
hold him come, Off - spring of the fav - ored one. Veil'd in flesh, the God-head see;
all he brings, Ris'n with heal - ing, in his wings. Mild he lays his glo - ry by,

Join the tri - umph of the skies; With th'an-gel - ic host pro-claim, "Christ is born in
Hail th'in - car - nate De - i - ty: Pleased, as man, with men to dwell, Je - sus, our Im -
Born that man no more may die: Born to raise the sons of earth, Born to give them

Beth - le - hem."
man - u - el! } Hark! the her - ald an - gels sing, "Glo - ry to the new - born King!"
se - cond birth.

My Faith Looks Up To Thee

OLIVET

LOWELL MASON

1. My faith looks up to Thee, Thou Lamb of Cal - va - ry, Sav - iour di - vine! Now hear me
2. May Thy rich grace im-part Strength to my faint - ing heart, My zeal in - spire! As Thou hast
3. While life's dark maze I tread, And griefs a - round me spread, Be Thou my Guide; Bid dark-ness

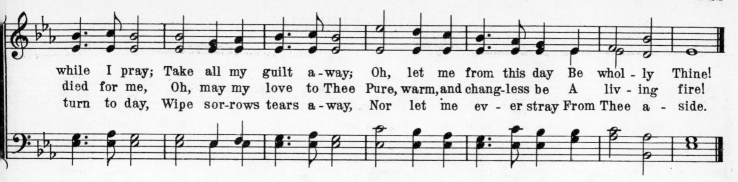

while I pray; Take all my guilt a-way; Oh, let me from this day Be whol-ly Thine!
died for me, Oh, may my love to Thee Pure, warm, and chang-less be A liv-ing fire!
turn to day, Wipe sor-rows tears a-way, Nor let me ev-er stray From Thee a-side.

Glorious Things Of Thee Are Spoken

AUSTRIA

JOSEPH HAYDN

1. Glo-rious things of thee are spo-ken, Zi-on, cit-y of our God;
2. See, the streams of liv-ing wa-ters, Spring-ing from e-ter-nal love,
3. Round each hab-i-ta-tion hov-'ring, See the cloud and fire ap-pear

He, whose word can-not be bro-ken, Form'd thee for His own a-bode;
Well sup-ply thy sons and daugh-ters, And all fear of want re-move.
For a glo-ry and a cov-'ring, Show-ing that the Lord is near;

On the Rock of A-ges found-ed, What can shake thy sure re-pose?
Who can faint while such a riv-er Ev-er flows their thirst t'as-suage?
Thus de-riv-ing from their ban-ner, Light by night, and shade by day.

With sal-va-tion's walls sur-round-ed, Thou may'st smile at all thy foes.
Grace which, like the Lord, the giv-er, Nev-er fails from age to age.
Safe they feed up-on the man-na Which He gives them when they pray.

Cradle Hymn

ISAAC WATTS

J. J. ROUSSEAU

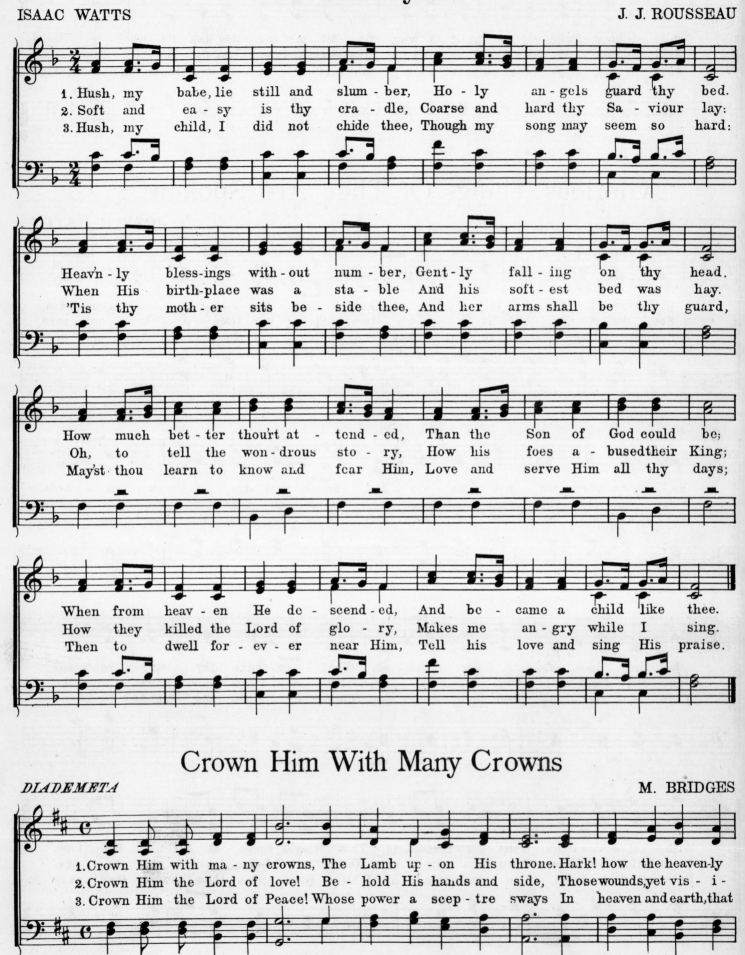

1. Hush, my babe, lie still and slum-ber, Ho-ly an-gels guard thy bed.
2. Soft and ea-sy is thy cra-dle, Coarse and hard thy Sa-viour lay:
3. Hush, my child, I did not chide thee, Though my song may seem so hard:

Heav'n-ly bless-ings with-out num-ber, Gent-ly fall-ing on thy head.
When His birth-place was a sta-ble And his soft-est bed was hay.
'Tis thy moth-er sits be-side thee, And her arms shall be thy guard,

How much bet-ter thou'rt at-tend-ed, Than the Son of God could be;
Oh, to tell the won-drous sto-ry, How his foes a-bused their King;
Mayst thou learn to know and fear Him, Love and serve Him all thy days;

When from heav-en He de-scend-ed, And be-came a child like thee.
How they killed the Lord of glo-ry, Makes me an-gry while I sing.
Then to dwell for-ev-er near Him, Tell his love and sing His praise.

Crown Him With Many Crowns

DIADEMETA

M. BRIDGES

1. Crown Him with ma-ny crowns, The Lamb up-on His throne. Hark! how the heaven-ly
2. Crown Him the Lord of love! Be-hold His hands and side, Those wounds, yet vis-i-
3. Crown Him the Lord of Peace! Whose power a scep-tre sways In heaven and earth, that

an - them drowns All mu - sic but its own! A - wake, my soul, and sing Of
ble a - bove, In beau - ty glo - ri - fied: No an - gel in the sky can
wars may cease, And all be prayer and praise. His reign shall know no end; And

Him who died for thee; And hail Him as thy match-less King Through all e - ter - ni - ty.
ful - ly bear that sight, But down-ward bends his wond-'ring eye At mys - ter - ies so bright.
round His pier-ced feet, Fair flowers of Par - a - dise ex - tend Their fra-grance ev - er sweet.

Come, Ye Disconsolate

THOS. MOORE

SAMUEL WEBBE

1. Come, ye dis - con - so - late! wher - e'er ye lan - guish, Come to the
2. Joy of the des - o - late! light of the stray - ing, Hope of the
3. Here see the bread of life: see wa - ters flow - ing Forth from the

mer - cy - seat, fer - vent - ly kneel: Here bring your wound - ed hearts,
pen - i - tent, fade - less and pure! Here speaks the Com - fort - er,
throne of God, pure from a - bove: Come to the feast of love;

here tell your an - guish; Earth has no sor - row that heav'n can - not heal.
ten - der - ly say - ing, Earth has no sor - row that heav'n can - not cure.
come, ev - er know - ing Earth has no sor - row but heav'n can re - move.

From Greenland's Icy Mountains

LOWELL MASON

MISSIONARY

1. From Green-land's i - cy moun-tains, From In - dia's cor - al strand,
2. What though the spi - cy breez - es Blow soft o'er Cey - lon's isle;
3. Shall we, whose souls are light - ed With wis-dom from on high,

Where Af - ric's sun - ny foun - tains Roll down their gold - en sand;
Though ev-'ry pros-pect pleas - es, And on - ly man is vile;
Shall we to men be - night - ed The lamp of life de - ny?

From many an an - cient riv - er, From many a palm - y plain,
In vain with lav - ish kind - ness, The gifts of God are strewn:
Sal - va - tion! Oh! sal - va - tion! The joy-ful sound pro - claim,

They call us to de - liv - er Their land from er - ror's chain.
The hea - then, in his blind - ness, Bows down to wood and stone.
Till earth's re - mot - est na - tion Has learned Mes - si - ah's name.

Brightest And Best

REGINALD HEBER

SAMUEL WEBBE

1. Bright - est and best of the sons of the morn - ing, Dawn on our
2. Cold on His cra - dle the dew-drops are shin - ing, Low lies His
3. Say, shall we yield Him, in cost - ly de - vo - tion O - dors of

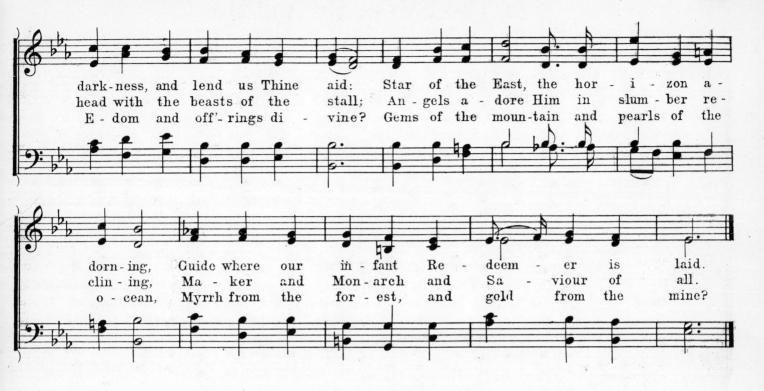

darkness, and lend us Thine aid: Star of the East, the hor-i-zon a-
head with the beasts of the stall; An-gels a-dore Him in slum-ber re-
E-dom and off'-rings di - vine? Gems of the moun-tain and pearls of the

dorn-ing, Guide where our in-fant Re-deem-er is laid.
clin-ing, Ma-ker and Mon-arch and Sa-viour of all.
o-cean, Myrrh from the for-est, and gold from the mine?

Blessed Saviour, Thee I Love

GEORGE DUFFIELD

1. Bless-ed Sav-iour, Thee I love, All my oth-er joys a-bove;
2. Once a-gain be-side the cross, All my gain I count but loss;
3. Bless-ed Sav-iour, Thine am I, Thine to live, and Thine to die;

All my hopes in Thee a-bide, Thou my hope, and naught be-side;
Earth-ly plea-sures fade a-way Clouds they are that hide my day.
Height, or depth, or earth-ly power, Ne'er shall hide my Sav-iour more;

Ev-er let my glo-ry be, On-ly, on-ly, on-ly Thee!
Hence, vain sha-dows! let me see Je-sus, cru-ci-fied for me.
Ev-'er shall my glo-ry be, On-ly, on-ly on-ly Thee!

In The Sweet By And By

S. FILLMORE BENNET

JOSEPH P. WEBSTER

With feeling

1. There's a land that is fair-er than day, And by faith we may see it a-
2. We shall sing on that beau-ti-ful shore The me-lo-di-ous songs of the
3. To our boun-ti-ful Fa-ther a-bove We will of-fer the trib-ute of

far, For the Fa-ther waits o-ver the way, To pre-pare us a dwell-ing place there.
blest, And our spir-its shall sor-row no more, Not a sigh for the bless-ings of rest.
praise For the glo-ri-ous gift of His love, And the bless-ings that hal-low our days!

In the sweet by and by we shall meet on that beau-ti-ful shore!
In the sweet by and by we shall sing on that beau-ti-ful shore!
In the sweet by and by we shall praise on that beau-ti-ful shore!

In the sweet by and by we shall meet on that beau-ti-ful shore!
In the sweet by and by we shall sing on that beau-ti-ful shore!
In the sweet by and by we shall praise on that beau-ti-ful shore!

Just As I Am

WOODWORTH

Wm. B. BRADBURY

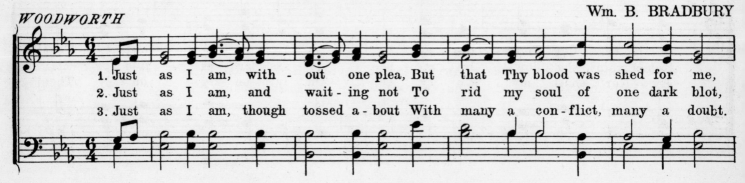

1. Just as I am, with-out one plea, But that Thy blood was shed for me,
2. Just as I am, and wait-ing not To rid my soul of one dark blot,
3. Just as I am, though tossed a-bout With many a con-flict, many a doubt.

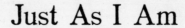

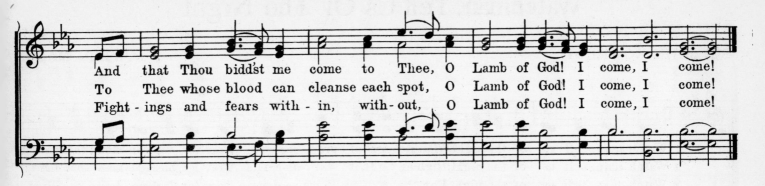

And that Thou bidd'st me come to Thee, O Lamb of God! I come, I come!
To Thee whose blood can cleanse each spot, O Lamb of God! I come, I come!
Fight-ings and fears with-in, with-out, O Lamb of God! I come, I come!

Jesus! The Very Thought Of Thee

JOHN B. DYKES

DULCIS MEMORIA

1. Je-sus! the ver-y thought of Thee With sweet-ness fills my breast;
2. Nor voice can sing, nor heart can frame, Nor can the mem-'ry find
3. O hope of ev-'ry con-trite heart! O joy of all the meek!

But sweet-er far Thy face to see, And in Thy pres-ence rest.
A sweet-er sound than Thy blest name, O Sav-iour of man-kind!
To those who fall, how kind Thou art! How good to those who seek!

How Gentle God's Commands

PHILLIP DODDRIDGE

H. G. NÄGELI

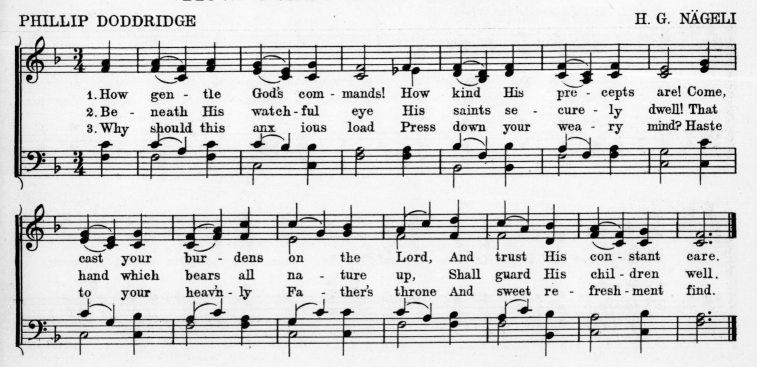

1. How gen-tle God's com-mands! How kind His pre-cepts are! Come,
2. Be-neath His watch-ful eye His saints se-cure-ly dwell! That
3. Why should this anx-ious load Press down your wea-ry mind? Haste

cast your bur-dens on the Lord, And trust His con-stant care.
hand which bears all na-ture up, Shall guard His chil-dren well.
to your heav'n-ly Fa-ther's throne And sweet re-fresh-ment find.

Watchman, Tell Us Of The Night

SIR JOHN BOWRING

LOWELL MASON

Before Jehovah's Awful Throne

ISAAC WATTS

M. A. VENUA

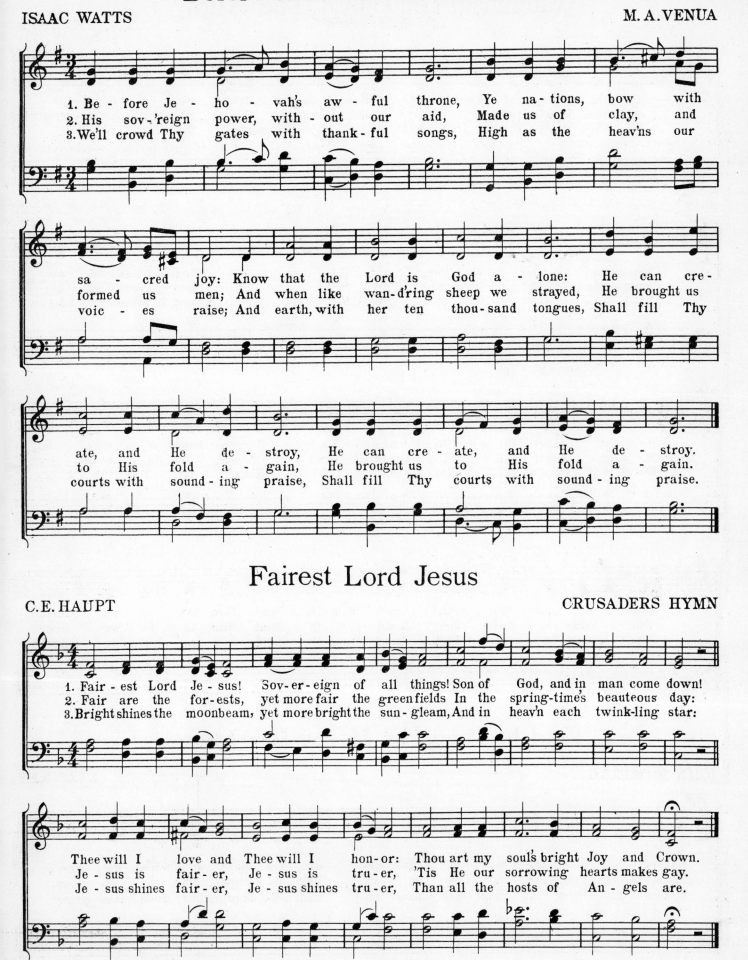

1. Be - fore Je - ho - vah's aw - ful throne, Ye na - tions, bow with
2. His sov - 'reign power, with - out our aid, Made us of clay, and
3. We'll crowd Thy gates with thank - ful songs, High as the heav'ns our

sa - cred joy: Know that the Lord is God a - lone: He can cre -
formed us men; And when like wan - d'ring sheep we strayed, He brought us
voic - es raise; And earth, with her ten thou - sand tongues, Shall fill Thy

ate, and He de - stroy, He can cre - ate, and He de - stroy.
to His fold a - gain, He brought us to His fold a - gain.
courts with sound - ing praise, Shall fill Thy courts with sound - ing praise.

Fairest Lord Jesus

C. E. HAUPT

CRUSADERS HYMN

1. Fair - est Lord Je - sus! Sov - er - eign of all things! Son of God, and in man come down!
2. Fair are the for - ests, yet more fair the green fields In the spring-time's beauteous day:
3. Bright shines the moonbeam, yet more bright the sun - gleam, And in heav'n each twink-ling star:

Thee will I love and Thee will I hon - or: Thou art my soul's bright Joy and Crown.
Je - sus is fair - er, Je - sus is tru - er, 'Tis He our sorrowing hearts makes gay.
Je - sus shines fair - er, Je - sus shines tru - er, Than all the hosts of An - gels are.

O Thou Joyful Day
(O Sanctissima)

B. M. SMUCKER

1. O thou joy-ful day, O thou bless-ed day, Ho-ly, peace-ful
2. O thou joy-ful day, O thou bless-ed day, Ho-ly, peace-ful
3. O thou joy-ful day, O thou bless-ed day, Ho-ly, peace-ful

Christ-mas-tide! O thou joy-ful day, O thou bless-ed day,
Christ-mas-tide! O thou joy-ful day, O thou bless-ed day,
Christ-mas-tide! O thou joy-ful day, O thou bless-ed day,

Ho-ly, peace-ful Christ-mas-tide! Earth's hopes a-wak-en,
Ho-ly, peace-ful Christ-mas-tide! Christ's light is beam-ing,
Ho-ly, peace-ful Christ-mas-tide! King of all glo-ry,

Christ life has tak-en, Laud Him, O laud Him on ev-'ry side.
Our souls re-deem-ing, Laud Him, O laud Him on ev-'ry side!
We bow be-fore Thee, Laud Him, O laud Him on ev-'ry side!

God Is Love, His Mercy Brightens

JOHN BOWRING

I. CONKEY

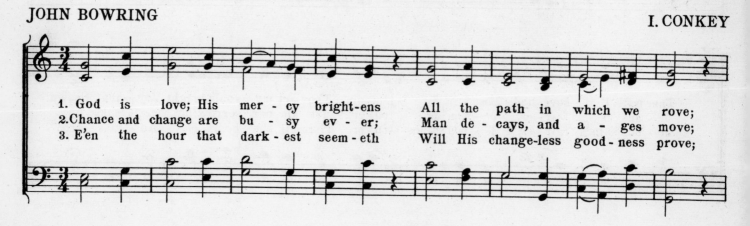

1. God is love; His mer-cy bright-ens All the path in which we rove;
2. Chance and change are bu-sy ev-er; Man de-cays, and a-ges move;
3. E'en the hour that dark-est seem-eth Will His change-less good-ness prove;

Bliss He wakes and woe He light-ens: God is wis-dom, God is love.
But His mer-cy wan-eth nev-er: God is wis-dom, God is love.
From the gloom His bright-ness stream-eth: God is wis-dom, God is love.

Come, Thou Fount Of Every Blessing

R. ROBINSON

JOHN WYETH

1. Come, Thou Fount of ev-'ry bless-ing, Tune my heart to sing Thy grace;
2. Here I'll raise my E - be - ne - zer Hith - er by Thy help I'm come,
3. Oh, to Grace, how great a deb - tor, Dai - ly I'm con-strained to be!

Streams of mer - cy, nev - er ceas - ing, Call for songs of loud - est praise.
And I hope, by Thy good plea - sure Safe - ly to ar - rive at home.
Let Thy good-ness as a fet - ter, Bind my wan - d'ring heart to Thee.

Teach me some mel - o - dious son - net, Sung by flam - ing tongues a - bove;
Je - sus sought me when a stran - ger, Wan - d'ring from the fold of God;
Prone to wan - der, Lord, I feel it, Prone to leave the God I love;

Praise the mount, I'm fixed up - on it! Mount of Thy re - deem - ing love.
He to res - cue me from dan - ger In - ter - posed His pre - cious blood.
Here's my heart, oh, take and seal it, Seal it for Thy courts a - bove.

Homeward Bound

W. F. WARREN

C. S. HARRINGTON

1. Out on an o-cean all bound-less we ride, We're home-ward bound,
2. Wild-ly the storm sweeps us on as it roars, We're home-ward bound,
3. In-to the har-bor of heav'n now we glide; We're home at last,

home-ward bound; Tossed on the waves of a rough, rest-less tide, We're home-ward
home-ward bound; Look! yon-der lie the bright heav-en-ly shores: We're home-ward
home at last; Soft-ly we drift on its bright sil-ver tide: We're home at

bound, home-ward bound. Far from the safe, qui-et har-bor we rode,
bound, home-ward bound. Stead-y O pi-lot! stand firm at the wheel,
last, home at last. Glo-ry to God! all our dan-gers are o'er,

Seek-ing our Fa-ther's ce-les-tial a-bode; Prom-ise of
Stead-y we soon shall out-weath-er the gale; Oh, how we
We stand se-cure on the glo-ri-fied shore; Glo-ry to

which on us each He be-stowed: We're home-ward bound, home-ward bound.
fly 'neath the loud-creak-ing sail! We're home-ward bound, home-ward bound.
God! we will shout ev-er more: We're home at last, home at last.

O Come All Ye Faithful

(Adeste Fideles)

J. READING

1. O come all ye faith - ful, Joy - ful and tri - um - phant, O
2. God of God, Light of Light
3. Sing choirs of an - gels, Sing in ex - ul - ta - tion,

come ye, O come ye to Beth - le - hem;
Lo! He ab - hors not the Vir - gins womb;
Sing, all ye ci - ti - zens of heav'n a - bove:

Come and be - hold Him Born the King of An - gels.
Ve - ry God, Be - got - ten, not cre - a - ted;
Glo - ry to God In the high - est;

After each verse

O come, let us a - dore Him, O come, let us a - dore Him, O

come, let us a - dore Him, Christ the Lord.

Come, Thou Almighty King

MOSCOW

FELICE GIARDINI

1. Come, Thou al-might-y King, Help us Thy name to sing, Help us to praise; Fa-ther! all
2. Come, Thou in-car-nate Word, Gird on Thy might-y sword, Our pray'r at-tend; Come, and Thy
3. Come, ho-ly Com-fort-er! Thy sa-cred wit-ness bear, In this glad hour: Thou who al-

glo - ri-ous, O'er all vic-to-ri-ous, Come and reign o-ver us, An-cient of days.
peo - ple bless, And give Thy word suc-cess, Spir-it of ho-li-ness! On us de-scend.
might - y art, Now rule in ev-'ry heart, And ne'er from us de-part, Spir-it of powr!

Blest Be The Tie That Binds

JOHN FAWCETT

H. G. NAGELI

1. Blest be the tie that binds Our hearts in Chris-tian love;
2. Be - fore our Fa-ther's throne, We pour our ar-dent prayers;
3. We share our mu-tual woes, Our mu-tual bur-dens bear;

The fel-low-ship of kin-dred minds Is like to that a-bove.
Our fears, our hopes, our aims are one, Our com-forts and our cares.
And oft-en for each oth-er flows The sym-pa-thiz-ing tear.

Come, Holy Spirit, Heavenly Dove

ST. AGNES

J. B. DYKES

mf

1. Come, Ho-ly Spir-it, Heaven-ly Dove, With all Thy quick-'ning power,
2. See how we grov-el here be-low, Fond of these earth-ly toys:
3. In vain we tune our life-less songs, In vain we strive to rise:

mf

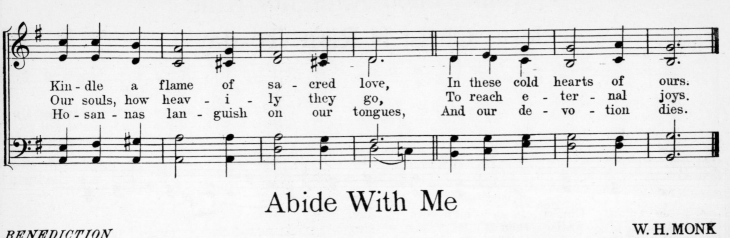

Kin - dle   a   flame   of   sa - cred   love,   In these   cold   hearts   of   ours.
Our souls, how   heav - i - ly   they   go,   To reach   e - ter - nal   joys.
Ho - san - nas   lan - guish   on   our   tongues,   And our   de - vo - tion   dies.

Abide With Me

BENEDICTION

W. H. MONK

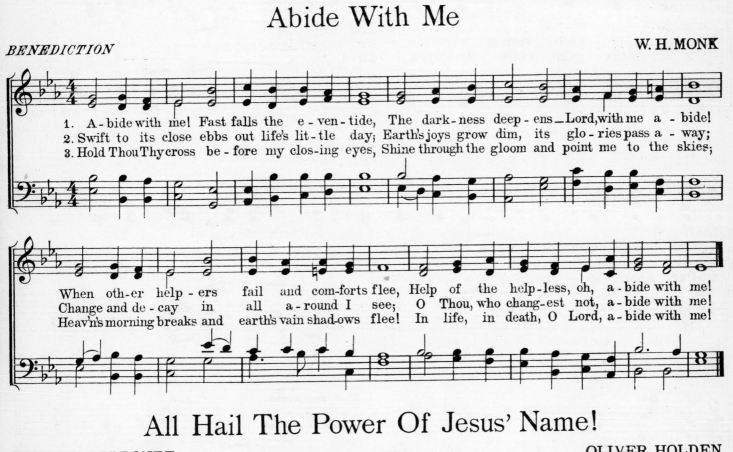

1. A - bide with me! Fast falls the e - ven-tide, The dark-ness deep-ens—Lord, with me a - bide!
2. Swift to its close ebbs out life's lit-tle day; Earth's joys grow dim, its glo - ries pass a - way;
3. Hold Thou Thy cross be - fore my clos-ing eyes, Shine through the gloom and point me to the skies;

When oth-er help - ers   fail and com-forts flee, Help of the help-less, oh, a - bide with me!
Change and de - cay   in   all a - round I see; O Thou, who chang-est not, a - bide with me!
Heav'n's morning breaks and   earth's vain shad-ows flee! In life, in death, O Lord, a - bide with me!

All Hail The Power Of Jesus' Name!

EDWARD PERRONET

OLIVER HOLDEN

1. All hail the pow'r of Je - sus' name! Let an-gels prostrate fall! Bring forth the roy - al di - a - dem,
2. Crown Him, ye morn-ing stars of light, Who fixed this earth-ly ball; Now hail the Strength of Is-rael's might,
3. Ye chos - en seed of Is-rael's race, Ye ran-somed from the fall, Hail Him who saves you by His grace,

And crown Him Lord of   all; Bring forth the roy - al di - a - dem, And crown Him Lord   of   all.
And crown Him Lord of   all; Now hail the Strength of Is rael's might, And crown Him Lord   of   all.
And crown Him Lord of   all; Hail Him who saves you by His grace, And crown Him Lord   of   all.

Jesus Christ Is Ris'n To-day

WORGAN

1. Je - sus Christ is ris'n to - day, Al - - le - lu - ia!
2. Hymns of praise then let us sing,
3. But the pains which He en - dured,

Our tri - umph - ant ho - ly day, Al - - le - lu - ia.
Un - to Christ, our heav'n - ly King,
Our sal - va - tion have pro - cured,

Who died once up - on the Cross, Al - - le - lu - ia.
Who en - dured the Cross and grave,
Now a - bove the sky He's King,

Suf - fer to re - deem our loss. Al - - le - lu - ia.
Sin - ners to re - deem and save.
Where the an - gels ev - er sing.